GREENBOOK®

Guide To

Department 56©

Including

The Original Snow Village©,

The Heritage Village Collection™,

&

Snowbabies©

Second Edition

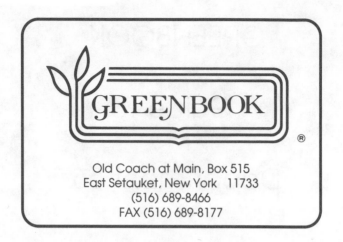

GREENBOOK

Old Coach at Main, Box 515
East Setauket, New York 11733
(516) 689-8466
FAX (516) 689-8177

ISBN 0-923628-13-4

Photography by Anthony Lopez, East End Studio, Miller Place, NY

Snow Village & Heritage Village Illustrations by Lynnwood Bohm
Snowbabies Illustrations by Lynnwood Bohm and John C. Phillips

Printed and bound by Searles Graphics, East Patchogue, New York

Published in East Setauket, NY

ACKNOWLEDGEMENTS

The GREENBOOK would like to thank –

Department 56 for assisting in the compilation of the factual information contained in this Guide.

Gift Creations Concepts for assisting in the compilation of the factual information contained in this Guide.

The collectors, dealers, exchanges, and newsletters across the country who supply us with information including secondary market status and prices.

A	5609 Park Avenue Townhouse	L	Busy Sidewalks figure
B	Red Brick Fire Station	M	Sutton Place Brownstones
C	Lighted Tree	N	Busy Sidewalks figure
D	Subway Entrance	O	Alpine Villager
E	Wrought Iron Village Gate with Fence	P	Chocolate Shoppe
F	Wong's in Chinatown	Q	Central Park Carriage
G	Bakery	R	Hank's Market
H	Ritz Hotel	S	Sleigh & Eight Tiny Reindeer
I	Town Square Gazebo	T	Tower Restaurant
J	The Cathedral	U	Old World Streetlamp
K	Village Evergreen Tree	V	City Hall

About the Artist

Lynnwood G. Bohm, was born on Long Island in 1948 into a family of artists.

She grew up spending summers in Southold and Greenport, Long Island and credits parts of her style to the Victorian beauty of the wonderful old homes and the natural forms of the seashore and night sky which she loves.

Other influences on her work come from her Grandfather, a well-known sculptor whose works grace many public buildings in Manhattan, and her father, a designer/modelmaker for a large toy corporation (but a true fisherman at heart).

Ms. Bohm is a graduate of The Fashion Institute of Technology in Manhattan and worked as a Fashion Illustrator for many years before settling on Long Island as a Graphic Designer. Her work has appeared in many major publications.

Ms. Bohm has one son, Jason, and an orange marmalade cat named Disney.

NOTE FROM THE PUBLISHER

Oh, the money I could get for the mini-series alone ...

... UPS drivers who know not to stop with packages if the spouse's car is in the driveway,

... "support groups for village addicts," a/k/a collector clubs,

... extensions built on the homes of otherwise normal folks, just so they can display their little lighted houses,

... grown adults who say "willage."

... something called "Real Plastic Snow®?" (I know, I read about the bleached cornflakes and mice too.)

If you own the First Edition of the Guide, you'll notice some changes with this, the Second Edition - most notably the addition of color photographs of many of the popular variations. To me, this section is like meeting someone in person you've only known over the phone - a face to go with the voice? Or, in this case, a picture to go with the often heard or advertised name? The "with" and "without" variations are the easiest - either he has a mustache or he doesn't, the window panes are there or they aren't... Mold changes are relatively easy too. But the subtle color variations? Let me start by saying the person we asked to find and purchase the different Dickens' Village Churches, by her own account, still hasn't recovered. A "green" Village Church? - we're talking a hint of a tint - if you're in natural light. That's not to say that somewhere out there there isn't one as green as green can be. Remember, these pieces are handpainted. But a strong argument could be made for the side that says why pay in the neighborhood of $350 for the "green" piece when a "dark" one can be obtained for less than half that figure? Or, if you prefer the lighter coloration, what is called "cream" sells for considerably less than the "green" and many experts can't tell them apart.

I still can't see the difference between the "lemon gold" and "cream" Ada's. Yet a co-worker could pick them out every time, try as we might to confuse her with our own version of the shell game.

The most reasonable words I've heard to date come from someone who's been in this business a very long time who simply said now and then he gets in an exquisite piece where everything about it is perfect. That being the case, he has to pay more for it and can sell it for a premium price. I'm with him.

This has been such a fun year. Thanks are owed to all of you who took time out from your busy schedules to drop us a note pointing out errors and omissions in the First Edition. It is in this way the Guide is fine tuned. Even still, I was planning on telling you how I think you're all nuts. But I decided to reconsider. As we speak, I have my own Mom out searching for the pink Cadillac...

Louise L. Patterson Langenfeld
Publisher

TABLE OF CONTENTS

HOW TO USE THIS GUIDE

The GREENBOOK ART CHART & LISTINGS contain exclusive GREENBOOK line drawings as well as specific factual information and GREENBOOK Market Prices for each piece.

Factual information includes Title, Description, Year Of Introduction, Item Number, Material, Is it part of a Set and if so the number of pieces comprising the Set, Is it Lighted?, Market Status or specific edition limit, and the Original Suggested Retail Price.

Secondary Market Prices, as reported by retailers and collectors, are included as well. Because there are so many factors based on individual judgements, and because prices can vary depending on time of year or section of the country, **GREENBOOK Market Prices are never an absolute number**. Use them as a benchmark.

The Guide is divided into three main sections: The Original Snow Village, The Heritage Village Collection, and Snowbabies. Within each section GREENBOOK Listings are in chronological date of introduction order. It's important to remember "the year of introduction indicates the year in which the piece was designed, sculpted, and copyrighted" and the piece is generally available to collectors the following calendar year.

Within each year the listings are in Department 56 Item Number order.

Each piece has been assigned a GREENBOOK ART CHART Number comprised of a coded alphabetic prefix (SV = Snow Village, CIC = Christmas In The City, etc.), followed by year of introduction, and then a sequential number.

If you know the name of the piece but not the year of introduction, use the Name/Department 56 Item Number/GREENBOOK Art Chart Number/Page Number Index in the back of the Guide to locate the piece.

Variations and comments are noted in the shaded area of each listing. And in most cases there's room for your own notes as well.

The Original Snow Village ©

SV76-1

MOUNTAIN LODGE
Bright colored skis lean against two-story lodge, upper windows painted to appear as lead panes, sunburst painted above door, snow laden tree at side.

SV76-2

GABLED COTTAGE
Four-peaked roof with two chimneys, curtained windows, ivy climbs walls to roof, welcome mat, door & several windows have wreath design, snow laden tree with bluebird.

SV76-3

THE INN
Two large brick chimneys, full length covered porch, welcome mat at timbered front doors, snow laden tree on one side, bright yellow door on opposite side.

SV76-4

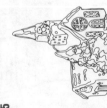

COUNTRY CHURCH
Vines and painted welcome on walls, short-spired, door ajar, circular upper windows, painted side windows, snow laden tree shades one wall.

SV76-5

STEEPLED CHURCH
One spire, large circular window over double wood front doors flanked by leaded lattice design windows, side Chapel, snow covered tree, bluebird on steeple.

SV76-6

SMALL CHALET
Two-story small gingerbread look home, flower box with snow covered plants set off large windows on upper story, bluebirds decorate corners of flower box, chimney, tree.

ART CHART #	NAME	ITEM #	MATERIAL	SET?	🔔	MARKET STATUS	ORIGINAL SRP	GREENBOOK MKT PRICE
	VARIATIONS/MISC/COLLECTOR NOTES							
SV76-1	MOUNTAIN LODGE	5001-3	Ceramic	NO	✓	RETIRED 1979	$ 20.00	$ 550.00
SV76-2	GABLED COTTAGE	5002-1	Ceramic	NO	✓	RETIRED 1979	20.00	475.00
SV76-3	THE INN	5003-9	Ceramic	NO	✓	RETIRED 1979	20.00	500.00
SV76-4	COUNTRY CHURCH	5004-7	Ceramic	NO	✓	RETIRED 1979	18.00	435.00
	Also known as "Wayside Chapel."							
SV76-5	STEEPLED CHURCH	5005-4	Ceramic	NO	✓	RETIRED 1979	25.00	675.00
SV76-6	SMALL CHALET	5006-2	Ceramic	NO	✓	RETIRED 1979	15.00	415.00
	Also known as "Gingerbread Chalet." Variation in number of flowers in boxes.							

CLIPBOARD
- Original pieces characterized by simple design, rough construction, and bright colors.
- All have attached snow laden evergreen trees with unique feature – bulb that lights house also lights tree.
- The "Gabled Cottage" and "The Inn" were the first Original Snow Village pieces to put out the welcome mats.

THE ORIGINAL SNOW VILLAGE

SV77-1

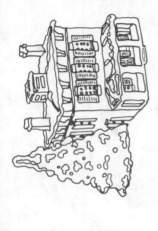

VICTORIAN HOUSE
Textured to portray shingles and clapboard. Steps lead up to front door.
Stained glass inserts above windows. Attached snow laden evergreen tree.

SV77-2

MANSION
White brick with porch supported by pillars, windows are shuttered,
two chimneys plus cupola on roof. Attached snow laden evergreen tree.

SV77-3

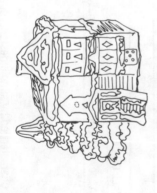

STONE CHURCH
Norman style stone building, steeple with ceramic bell.
Double doors with circular window above, snow laden evergreen tree.

ART CHART #	NAME	ITEM #	MATERIAL	SET?	⚲	MARKET STATUS	ORIGINAL SRP	GREENBOOK MKT PRICE
	VARIATIONS/MISC/COLLECTOR NOTES							
SV77-1	VICTORIAN HOUSE	5007-0	Ceramic	NO	✓	RETIRED 1979	$ 30.00	$ 485.00
	Variations in color and with & without birds.							
SV77-2	MANSION	5008-8	Ceramic	NO	✓	RETIRED 1979	30.00	600.00
SV77-3	STONE CHURCH	5009-6	Ceramic	NO	✓	RETIRED 1979	35.00	715.00
	This is the original Stone Church. See 1979, #5059-1 (SV79-6) and 1982, #5083-0 (SV82-10).							

CLIPBOARD
- Broader range of architectural styles, moved away from simple country village style.
- New building materials.
- Again, all had attached snow laden evergreen trees.

SV78-1

HOMESTEAD
Old fashioned farmhouse, front porch full length of house. Second floor bay windows. Triple window in front gable. Attached tree.

SV78-2

GENERAL STORE
Full length porch supported by pillars. Sign above porch. Christmas tree on porch roof. Store supplied food, postal service, & gas.

SV78-3

CAPE COD
Steep gabled roof with chimney, small dormer, and painted landscaping. Attached snow laden tree.

SV78-4

NANTUCKET
Yellow cottage with green roof. Small front porch, attached greenhouse/sunroom on side, attached snow laden tree.

SV78-5

SKATING RINK/ DUCK POND SET
Snowman, log pile, large snow laden tree.
&
Park bench, birds, large snow laden tree.

SV78-6

SMALL DOUBLE TREES
Small lighted snow laden trees with birds.

ART CHART #	NAME	ITEM #	MATERIAL	SET?	⊕	MARKET STATUS	ORIGINAL SRP	GREENBOOK MKT PRICE
	VARIATIONS/MISC/COLLECTOR NOTES							
SV78-1	HOMESTEAD	5011-2	Ceramic	NO	✓	RETIRED 1984	$ 30.00	$ 310.00
SV78-2	GENERAL STORE	5012-0	Ceramic	NO	✓	RETIRED 1980	25.00	500.00
	Variations in color and sign lettering.							
SV78-3	CAPE COD	5013-8	Ceramic	NO	✓	RETIRED 1980	20.00	385.00
SV78-4	NANTUCKET	5014-6	Ceramic	NO	✓	RETIRED 1986	25.00	250.00
SV78-5	SKATING RINK/ DUCK POND SET	5015-3	Ceramic	SET OF 2	✓	RETIRED 1979	16.00	1200.00
	One of first non-house accessory pcs. Trees were attached directly to pond bases - their size and weight caused frequent breakage, therefore retired in 1979. Revised skating pond in 1982, #5017-2 (SV82-1), with trees molded separately. Variation: blue birds and red birds.							
SV78-6	SMALL DOUBLE TREES	5016-1	Ceramic	NO	✓	RETIRED 1989	13.50	48.00
	One of the first non-house accessory pieces. Variation: with blue birds in 1979, GREENBOOK MARKET PRICE $150.							

CLIPBOARD
• New designs reflected a regional influence (New England).

16

THE ORIGINAL SNOW VILLAGE

SV79-1

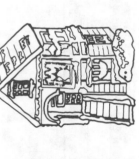

VICTORIAN
Steps lead to covered porch entry, three story turret, small balcony on third floor front room.

SV79-2

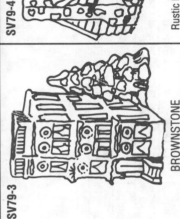

KNOB HILL
Three story San Francisco-style Victorian row house, steep steps to entry level.

SV79-3

BROWNSTONE
Three stories with wreath trimmed bay windows on all floors, overall flat roof.

SV79-4

LOG CABIN
Rustic log house with stone chimney, roof extends to cover porch, log pile at side, skis by door.

SV79-5

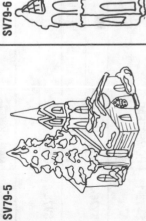

COUNTRYSIDE CHURCH
White clapboard church with central bell steeple, attached tree has all lower branches pruned.

SV79-6

STONE CHURCH
Steeple attached to one side has separate entry. Circular window above front doors.

SV79-7

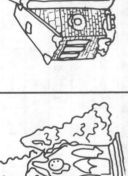

SCHOOL HOUSE
American flag flies from roof peak above red brick one-room school.

SV79-8

TUDOR HOUSE
Brick chimney and fireplace on simple L-shaped timber trimmed home, split-shingle roof.

ART CHART #	NAME	ITEM #	MATERIAL	SET?	🔔	MARKET STATUS	ORIGINAL SRP	GREENBOOK MKT PRICE
	VARIATIONS/MISC/COLLECTOR NOTES							
SV79-1	VICTORIAN	5054-2	Ceramic	NO	✓	RETIRED 1982	$ 30.00	$ 440.00
	Variations in color and exterior finish.							
SV79-2	KNOB HILL	5055-9	Ceramic	NO	✓	RETIRED 1981	30.00	350.00
	Two color variations: grey with black roof and yellow.							
SV79-3	BROWNSTONE	5056-7	Ceramic	NO	✓	RETIRED 1981	36.00	495.00
	Variations in color.							
SV79-4	LOG CABIN	5057-5	Ceramic	NO	✓	RETIRED 1981	22.00	475.00
SV79-5	COUNTRYSIDE CHURCH	5058-3	Ceramic	NO	✓	RETIRED 1984	27.50	295.00
	For no snow version see MEADOWLAND 1979, #5051-8.							
SV79-6	STONE CHURCH	5059-1	Ceramic	NO	✓	RETIRED 1980	32.00	850.00
	Height is 8.5". See also 1977, #5009-6 (SV77-3) and 1982, #5083-0 (SV82-10).							
SV79-7	SCHOOL HOUSE	5060-9	Ceramic*	NO	✓	RETIRED 1982	30.00	360.00
	First design to feature the American flag. *Metal flag.							
SV79-8	TUDOR HOUSE	5061-7	Ceramic	NO	✓	RETIRED 1981	25.00	385.00

THE ORIGINAL SNOW VILLAGE

1979 1979

SV79-9

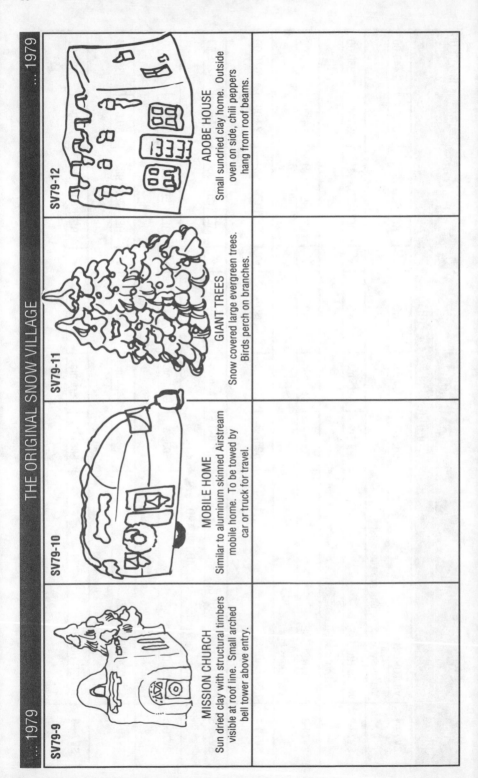

MISSION CHURCH
Sun dried clay with structural timbers visible at roof line. Small arched bell tower above entry.

SV79-10

MOBILE HOME
Similar to aluminum skinned Airstream mobile home. To be towed by car or truck for travel.

SV79-11

GIANT TREES
Snow covered large evergreen trees. Birds perch on branches.

SV79-12

ADOBE HOUSE
Small sundried clay home. Outside oven on side, chili peppers hang from roof beams.

ART CHART #	NAME	ITEM #	MATERIAL	SET?	🔔	MARKET STATUS	ORIGINAL SRP	GREENBOOK MKT PRICE
	VARIATIONS/MISC/COLLECTOR NOTES							
SV79-9	MISSION CHURCH	5062-5	Ceramic	NO	✓	RETIRED 1980	$ 30.00	$ 950.00
SV79-10	MOBILE HOME	5063-3	Ceramic	NO	✓	RETIRED 1980	18.00	1625.00
SV79-11	GIANT TREES	5065-8	Ceramic	NO	✓	RETIRED 1982	20.00	295.00
SV79-12	ADOBE HOUSE	5066-6	Ceramic	NO	✓	RETIRED 1980	18.00	2000.00

CLIPBOARD
• First year of retirement.

20

1980

THE ORIGINAL SNOW VILLAGE

1980

SV80-1

CATHEDRAL CHURCH
Central dome with two shorter bell towers.

SV80-2

STONE MILL HOUSE
Waterwheel on dark weathered stone block mill, bag of grain hangs from block and tackle, another bag propped by door.

SV80-3

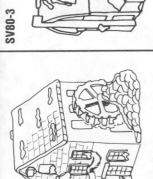

COLONIAL FARM HOUSE
Wide front porch, two front dormers in attic, symmetrical layout of windows.

SV80-4

TOWN CHURCH
Short bell tower rises from central nave area, attached tree tucks in close to side chapel.

SV80-5

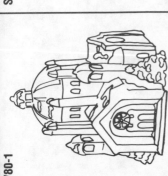

TRAIN STATION WITH 3 TRAIN CARS
Station clock over entry door, two small wings on either side of main room, brick and timbered design.
Train — engine, passenger car, baggage/mail caboose. "G&N RR" on all cars.

ART CHART #	NAME	ITEM #	MATERIAL	SET?	🔔	MARKET STATUS	ORIGINAL SRP	GREENBOOK MKT PRICE
	VARIATIONS/MISC/COLLECTOR NOTES							
SV80-1	CATHEDRAL CHURCH	5067-4	Ceramic*	NO	✓	RETIRED 1981	$ 36.00	$ 825.00
	Production problems (fragile domes) forced retirement after one year. *Stained glass windows are acrylic.							
SV80-2	STONE MILL HOUSE	5068-2	Ceramic	NO	✓	RETIRED 1982	30.00	635.00
	Separate bag of oats hung with wire.							
SV80-3	COLONIAL FARM HOUSE	5070-9	Ceramic	NO	✓	RETIRED 1982	30.00	425.00
SV80-4	TOWN CHURCH	5071-7	Ceramic	NO	✓	RETIRED 1982	33.00	385.00
SV80-5	TRAIN STATION WITH 3 TRAIN CARS	5085-6	Ceramic	SET OF 4	✓	RETIRED 1985	100.00	375.00
	Variation: Original had 6 window panes, round window in door. Brick on front, not sides. Revised had 8 window panes, 2 square windows in door, brick on front and sides. First Original Snow Village train and station design. All four pieces lit.							

CLIPBOARD
• Few introductions due to large number of ongoing pieces.
• Understamping accompanied adhesive stickers.

22

SV81-1

WOODEN CLAPBOARD

White house with green roof and trim and wraparound porch. Red brick chimney.

SV81-2

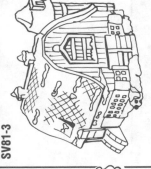

ENGLISH COTTAGE

Thatched roof and timbered frame, two chimneys. 1 1/2 stories. Roof comes down to meet top of first story.

SV81-3

BARN

Red barn and silo. Grey roof, two vents on roof ridge, root cellar on side, hay loft over animals and equipment.

SV81-4

CORNER STORE

Red brick with one large display window, entry door on corner, bay window in family living area, shutters on windows, shingled roof.

SV81-5

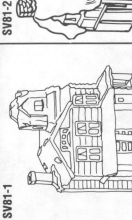

BAKERY

Bakery store beneath family living area, white with green trim, half turret form gives unique angle to front and second story bay window.

SV81-6

ENGLISH CHURCH

Steep pitched roof, side chapel, steeple topped by gold cross, arched windows, triangular window in gable above entry double doors.

SV81-7

LARGE SINGLE TREE

One snow covered evergreen tree. Birds perch on branches.

ART CHART #	NAME	ITEM #	MATERIAL	SET?	❤	MARKET STATUS	ORIGINAL SRP	GREENBOOK MKT PRICE
	VARIATIONS/MISC/COLLECTOR NOTES							
SV81-1	WOODEN CLAPBOARD	5072-5	Ceramic	NO	✓	RETIRED 1984	$ 32.00	$ 320.00
SV81-2	ENGLISH COTTAGE	5073-3	Ceramic	NO	✓	RETIRED 1982	25.00	350.00
	Variations in color of thatched roof.							
SV81-3	BARN	5074-1	Ceramic	NO	✓	RETIRED 1984	32.00	425.00
SV81-4	CORNER STORE	5076-8	Ceramic	NO	✓	RETIRED 1983	30.00	260.00
SV81-5	BAKERY	5077-6	Ceramic	NO	✓	RETIRED 1983	30.00	275.00
	This is the original Bakery. The same Item # was used for the 1986 Bakery (SV86-15) – a new and different design.							
SV81-6	ENGLISH CHURCH	5078-4	Ceramic	NO	✓	RETIRED 1982	30.00	375.00
	The Cross is separate and inserts into the steeple.							
SV81-7	LARGE SINGLE TREE	5080-6	Ceramic	NO	✓	RETIRED 1989	17.00	50.00

24

THE ORIGINAL SNOW VILLAGE

SV82-1

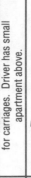

SKATING POND
Snowman on edge of small snow covered skating pond. Tree trunks piled together provide seating. Two evergreen trees complete the set.

SV82-2

STREET CAR
Bright yellow with green "Main Street" sign on side. #2 car, hook-up on top for pole to connect to electric power.

SV82-3

CENTENNIAL HOUSE
Two story clapboard, square tower, carved and curved window frames, "wooden" balcony & porch.

SV82-4

CARRIAGE HOUSE
Bright lamps flank entry to storage area for carriages. Driver has small apartment above.

SV82-5

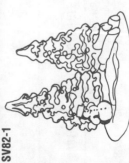

PIONEER CHURCH
Simple design appears to be of wood construction, front notice board sends joy to all who pass, short steeple on front of roof ridge.

SV82-6

SWISS CHALET
Stone base walls support timber upper stories. Upper floor has front balcony with railing and is enclosed by roof overhang. Unusual roof.

SV82-7

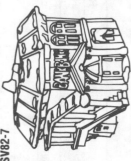

BANK
Corner building with entry by revolving door. Outside covered stairway leads to second story. Sign becomes part of corner design.

SV82-8

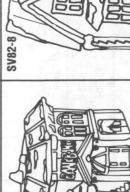

GABLED HOUSE
Shingled house with four gabled roof, two small covered porches, one lower and one upper window to each side.

ART CHART #	NAME	ITEM #	MATERIAL	SET?	🕊	MARKET STATUS	ORIGINAL SRP	GREENBOOK MKT PRICE
SV82-1	SKATING POND	5017-2	Ceramic	SET OF 2	✓	RETIRED 1984	$ 25.00	$ 350.00
	VARIATIONS/MISC/COLLECTOR NOTES							
	Replaces the Skating Rink/Duck Pond Set (1978, #5015-3, SV78-5). Has two trees. Trees are separate from the pond.							
SV82-2	STREET CAR	5019-9	Ceramic	NO	✓	RETIRED 1984	16.00	350.00
SV82-3	CENTENNIAL HOUSE	5020-2	Ceramic	NO	✓	RETIRED 1984	32.00	365.00
SV82-4	CARRIAGE HOUSE	5021-0	Ceramic	NO	✓	RETIRED 1984	28.00	315.00
SV82-5	PIONEER CHURCH	5022-9	Ceramic	NO	✓	RETIRED 1984	30.00	355.00
SV82-6	SWISS CHALET	5023-7	Ceramic	NO	✓	RETIRED 1984	28.00	450.00
SV82-7	BANK	5024-5	Ceramic	NO	✓	RETIRED 1983	32.00	635.00
SV82-8	GABLED HOUSE	5081-4	Ceramic	NO	✓	RETIRED 1983	30.00	400.00
	Variations in color. Same Item # was used for the 1987 Red Barn (SV87-7). Early release to Gift Creations Concepts.							

THE ORIGINAL SNOW VILLAGE

SV82-9

FLOWER SHOP
Flower boxes rest outside by large display window. Rolled up awnings above front windows.

SV82-10

NEW STONE CHURCH
Long nave with side chapel, stone block construction, steeple rises on side opposite chapel. Front has arched windows and two lamps.

ART CHART #	NAME	ITEM #	MATERIAL	SET?	♥ ▪	MARKET STATUS	ORIGINAL SRP	GREENBOOK MKT PRICE
SV82-9	FLOWER SHOP	5082-2	Ceramic	NO	✓	RETIRED 1983	$ 25.00	$ 450.00
	VARIATIONS/MISC/COLLECTOR NOTES							
	Variations in color. Same Item # was used for the 1987 Jefferson School (SV87-8).							
SV82-10	NEW STONE CHURCH	5083-0	Ceramic	NO	✓	RETIRED 1984	32.00	325.00
	Early release to Gift Creations Concepts.							

28

THE ORIGINAL SNOW VILLAGE

SV83-1

TOWN HALL

Brick and stone, two corner covered side entries, symmetrical design (window over window), steeple above front main wall.

SV83-2

GROCERY

Red brick, full painted display windows, decorative cornice trim above/below front windows. Outside staircase leads to family quarters.

SV83-3

VICTORIAN COTTAGE

Ornate carved woodwork on house front, ornamental arched entry design. First floor French windows separated by pillars.

SV83-4

GOVERNOR'S MANSION

Brick, metal ironwork featured on roof cupola, wide entry steps, repetitive design above door, second story, and central attic windows.

SV83-5

TURN OF THE CENTURY

Steps lead to covered entry, front triangular ornate design crowns front gable, squared turret rises from left front corner and ends in highest roof peak.

SV83-6

GINGERBREAD HOUSE

Designed like a Christmas edible treat. Cookies trim sides while candy canes and sugar heart decorate roof.

SV83-7

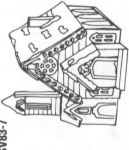
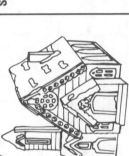

VILLAGE CHURCH

Stone steps lead to double carved doors, design repeats on roof trim. Steeple has long narrow openings. Pointed arch windows are featured.

SV83-8

GOTHIC CHURCH

Stone block, steeple rises straight from large double doors ending in a cross. Bell chamber has ornate grillwork. Smaller entry doors flank central area repeating design.

ART CHART #	NAME	ITEM #	MATERIAL	SET?	✏	MARKET STATUS	ORIGINAL SRP	GREENBOOK MKT PRICE
	VARIATIONS/MISC/COLLECTOR NOTES							
SV83-1	TOWN HALL	5000-8	Ceramic	NO	✓	RETIRED 1984	$ 32.00	$ 300.00
	Ceramic bell in tower.							
SV83-2	GROCERY	5001-6	Ceramic	NO	✓	RETIRED 1985	35.00	325.00
SV83-3	VICTORIAN COTTAGE	5002-4	Ceramic	NO	✓	RETIRED 1984	35.00	375.00
SV83-4	GOVERNOR'S MANSION	5003-2	Ceramic*	NO	✓	RETIRED 1985	32.00	285.00
	*Featured metal trim on front tower.							
SV83-5	TURN OF THE CENTURY	5004-0	Ceramic	NO	✓	RETIRED 1986	36.00	265.00
SV83-6	GINGERBREAD HOUSE	5025-3	Ceramic	NO		RETIRED 1984	24.00	370.00
SV83-7	VILLAGE CHURCH	5026-1	Ceramic	NO	✓	RETIRED 1984	30.00	330.00
	Early release to Gift Creations Concepts.							
SV83-8	GOTHIC CHURCH	5028-8	Ceramic	NO	✓	RETIRED 1986	36.00	250.00

SV83-9

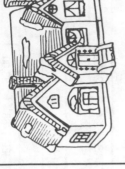

PARSONAGE

Tower rises above entry. Ornate coping on front gable topped by Cross. Coping details repeated around windows, doors, and small balcony. Community rooms on first floor, family lives upstairs.

SV83-10

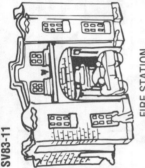

WOODEN CHURCH

White clapboard, crossed timber design repeats over door, roof peak, and steeple. Side chapel has separate entry door.

SV83-11

FIRE STATION

Central doors open to reveal red fire truck. Brick columns from base to roof add to sturdy look. Dalmatian sits by entry ready when necessary.

SV83-12

ENGLISH TUDOR

Stucco finish. Brick chimneys. Three front roof peaks create front gable design.

SV83-13

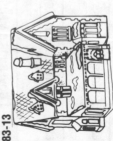

CHATEAU

First story large windows which include front and side bow windows are a feature. Diamond design on roof shingles, stone for walls, cylindrical chimney with domed flue cap. Front dormers and side peaks exhibit ornate carved design.

ART CHART #	NAME	ITEM #	MATERIAL	SET?	☺	MARKET STATUS	ORIGINAL SRP	GREENBOOK MKT PRICE
			VARIATIONS/MISC/COLLECTOR NOTES					
SV83-9	PARSONAGE	5029-6	Ceramic	NO	✓	RETIRED 1985	$ 35.00	$ 375.00
SV83-10	WOODEN CHURCH	5031-8	Ceramic	NO	✓	RETIRED 1985	30.00	400.00
SV83-11	FIRE STATION	5032-6	Ceramic	NO	✓	RETIRED 1984	32.00	675.00
	Variation: without dog.							
SV83-12	ENGLISH TUDOR	5033-4	Ceramic	NO	✓	RETIRED 1985	30.00	300.00
SV83-13	CHATEAU	5084-9	Ceramic	NO	✓	RETIRED 1984	35.00	375.00
	Early release to Gift Creations Concepts.							

THE ORIGINAL SNOW VILLAGE

SV84-1

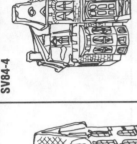

MAIN STREET HOUSE
White and green 1 1/2 story house. Clapboard lower story with timbered upper story, two lamps outside front door.

SV84-2

STRATFORD HOUSE
Vertical ornamental timbers featured, gables all rise to same height.

SV84-3

HAVERSHAM HOUSE
All gables, balconies, porch, decorated with ornately carved woodwork.

SV84-4

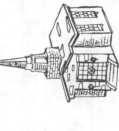

GALENA HOUSE
Steps lead to double entry doors of brick home. Bay window fills one side. Second floor incorporated into roof construction.

SV84-5

RIVER ROAD HOUSE
White house, large and grand with many windows, first floor front windows are highlighted with half circle paned glass above them, side bay windows project out from house wall.

SV84-6

DELTA HOUSE
Brick house with balcony above wrap-around porch which is separate from entry. Porch design is repeated where roof and brick meet and on turret.

SV84-7

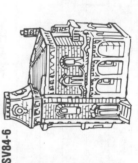

BAYPORT
Corner entry with a turret addition positioned between the two main wings of two story house.

SV84-8

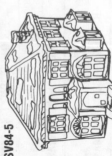

CONGREGATIONAL CHURCH
Brick with fieldstone front. Stone repeated on steeple. Louver vents on belfry.

ART CHART #	NAME	ITEM #	MATERIAL	SET?	☺	MARKET STATUS	ORIGINAL SRP	GREENBOOK MKT PRICE
SV84-1	MAIN STREET HOUSE	5005-9	Ceramic	NO	✓	RETIRED 1986	$ 27.00	$ 250.00
	Early release to Gift Creations Concepts.							
SV84-2	STRATFORD HOUSE	5007-5	Ceramic	NO	✓	RETIRED 1986	28.00	225.00
SV84-3	HAVERSHAM HOUSE	5008-3	Ceramic	NO	✓	RETIRED 1987	37.00	240.00
	Early release to Gift Creations Concepts.							
SV84-4	GALENA HOUSE	5009-1	Ceramic	NO	✓	RETIRED 1985	32.00	330.00
SV84-5	RIVER ROAD HOUSE	5010-5	Ceramic	NO	✓	RETIRED 1987	36.00	150.00
	Early release to Gift Creations Concepts.							
SV84-6	DELTA HOUSE	5012-1	Ceramic	NO	✓	RETIRED 1986	32.00	325.00
	"Iron works" atop tower not shown.							
SV84-7	BAYPORT	5015-6	Ceramic	NO	✓	RETIRED 1986	30.00	230.00
SV84-8	CONGREGATIONAL CHURCH	5034-2	Ceramic	NO	✓	RETIRED 1985	28.00	360.00

VARIATIONS/MISC/COLLECTOR NOTES

THE ORIGINAL SNOW VILLAGE

SV84-9

TRINITY CHURCH

Steeples of different heights, clerestory windows to bring additional light to central nave, two large wreaths by front doors.

SV84-10

SUMMIT HOUSE

Corner house features rounded turret, large entry door with side lights, cornices appear to support roof edge. Each second story window capped by a molded projection.

SV84-11

NEW SCHOOL HOUSE

Two story schoolhouse with bell tower and clock.

SV84-12

PARISH CHURCH

White country church with unique three level steeple. Arched windows, red door, circular window over entry.

ART CHART #	NAME	ITEM #	MATERIAL	SET?	♥	MARKET STATUS	ORIGINAL SRP	GREENBOOK MKT PRICE
	VARIATIONS/MISC/COLLECTOR NOTES							
SV84-9	TRINITY CHURCH	5035-0	Ceramic	NO	✓	RETIRED 1986	$ 32.00	$ 265.00
SV84-10	SUMMIT HOUSE	5036-9	Ceramic	NO	✓	RETIRED 1985	28.00	375.00
SV84-11	NEW SCHOOL HOUSE	5037-7	Ceramic*	NO	✓	RETIRED 1986	35.00	270.00
	*Separate flag - wooden pole, paper flag (not shown).							
SV84-12	PARISH CHURCH	5039-3	Ceramic	NO	✓	RETIRED 1986	32.00	345.00

SV85-1

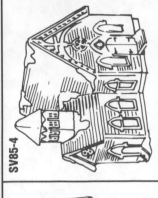

STUCCO BUNGALOW

Two story small house with one roof dormer as mini tower, second dormer features timbered design. Entry door built into archway under a low roof peak. Wreath and garland decorate door.

SV85-2

WILLIAMSBURG HOUSE

Traditional two story colonial, all windows shuttered, three dormers, two chimneys, covered entry topped by second floor balcony.

SV85-3

PLANTATION HOUSE

Entry features two story wood columns, three dormers, two chimneys, four first floor front windows have canopies.

SV85-4

CHURCH OF THE OPEN DOOR

Steeple is on side chapel. Design over front entry above circular window has small repeated motif on eaves.

SV85-5

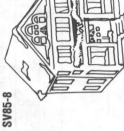

SPRUCE PLACE

Victorian with windowed turret rising above covered porch. Decorative molding above porch, windows, dormer. Circular window over porch decorated with wreath.

SV85-6

DUPLEX

A two-family house with shared entry. Each family had up/down rooms and a bay window. Design has small second story balcony and roof dormers.

SV85-7

DEPOT AND TRAIN WITH 2 TRAIN CARS

Two wings connected by a central area, each wing has its own chimney, corners of building fortified with stone blocks.

SV85-8

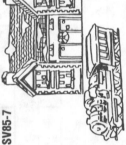

RIDGEWOOD

Porches run length of both first and second story. First floor front windows are arched and design is repeated over front door and on attic windows.

ART CHART #	NAME	ITEM #	MATERIAL	SET?	🔔	MARKET STATUS	ORIGINAL SRP	GREENBOOK MKT PRICE
	VARIATIONS/MISC/COLLECTOR NOTES							
SV85-1	STUCCO BUNGALOW	5045-8	Ceramic	NO	✓	RETIRED 1986	$ 30.00	$ 375.00
SV85-2	WILLIAMSBURG HOUSE	5046-6	Ceramic	NO	✓	RETIRED 1988	37.00	110.00
SV85-3	PLANTATION HOUSE	5047-4	Ceramic	NO	✓	RETIRED 1987	37.00	95.00
SV85-4	CHURCH OF THE OPEN DOOR	5048-2	Ceramic	NO	✓	RETIRED 1988	34.00	105.00
SV85-5	SPRUCE PLACE	5049-0	Ceramic	NO	✓	RETIRED 1988	33.00	315.00
SV85-6	DUPLEX	5050-4	Ceramic	NO	✓	RETIRED 1987	35.00	105.00
SV85-7	DEPOT AND TRAIN WITH 2 TRAIN CARS	5051-2	Ceramic	SET OF 4	✓	RETIRED 1988	65.00	125.00
	Train is non-lighting. Variations in color and depot exterior finish. Second Original Snow Village train and station design. Coal car has plastic bag of coal.							
SV85-8	RIDGEWOOD	5052-0	Ceramic	NO	✓	RETIRED 1987	35.00	130.00

THE ORIGINAL SNOW VILLAGE

SV86-1

WAVERLY PLACE

Ornate Victorian home has two different turret-like window designs. First story capped by molding and roof shingles creating unique bowed window. Second story features half moon window highlights and carved moldings.

SV86-2

TWIN PEAKS

Two matching three story stone turrets, a multitude of windows on each story soften fortress look. Red entry doors reached by wide steps.

SV86-3

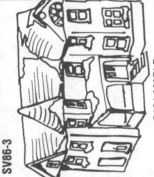

2101 MAPLE

Brick two story home. Side of front porch built out from stone turret. Two story bay windows capped by half circle window.

SV86-4

LINCOLN PARK DUPLEX

Two family attached home. Each has a two story bay windows and share a front door. Floor plan unique feature is placement of chimneys – as if floor plans reversed, one is at front, other is at rear.

SV86-5

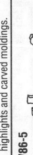

SONOMA HOUSE

Flavor of Southwest. Stucco walls, red roof. Decorative curved front rises up two and a half stories. Square turret adjacent to front door capped by same design which repeats on chimney.

SV86-6

HIGHLAND PARK HOUSE

Brick, timbered, and gabled house brings English Tudor design to cozy home. Rounded arch front door repeats theme in two windows in mid roof gable. Brick chimney on side. Layout of roof shingles add to English flavor.

SV86-7

BEACON HILL HOUSE

A row house, typical of urban Boston, MA neighborhoods. House has a solid compact look. Features bay windows on first and second story highlighted by paneled framing. Balcony on other front window also serves as canopy over oval paned front door.

SV86-8

PACIFIC HEIGHTS HOUSE

A West Coast row house that appears tall and narrow based on repeated vertical theme of front porch/balcony support columns. Motif repeated on windows and reinforced by pointed arch and roof line.

ART CHART #	NAME	ITEM #	MATERIAL	SET?	⬤	MARKET STATUS	ORIGINAL SRP	GREENBOOK MKT PRICE
SV86-1	WAVERLY PLACE	5041-5	Ceramic	NO	✓	RETIRED 1986	$ 35.00	$ 300.00
	VARIATIONS/MISC/COLLECTOR NOTES							
	Early release to Gift Creations Concepts, Fall 1985.							
SV86-2	TWIN PEAKS	5042-3	Ceramic	NO	✓	RETIRED 1986	32.00	285.00
	Early release to Gift Creations Concepts, Fall 1985.							
SV86-3	2101 MAPLE	5043-1	Ceramic	NO	✓	RETIRED 1986	32.00	330.00
	Early release to Gift Creations Concepts, Fall 1985.							
SV86-4	LINCOLN PARK DUPLEX	5060-1	Ceramic	NO	✓	RETIRED 1988	33.00	115.00
SV86-5	SONOMA HOUSE	5062-8	Ceramic	NO	✓	RETIRED 1988	33.00	110.00
	Early release to Gift Creations Concepts, Fall 1986.							
SV86-6	HIGHLAND PARK HOUSE	5063-6	Ceramic	NO	✓	RETIRED 1988	35.00	105.00
	Early release to Gift Creations Concepts, Fall 1986.							
SV86-7	BEACON HILL HOUSE	5065-2	Ceramic	NO	✓	RETIRED 1988	31.00	120.00
SV86-8	PACIFIC HEIGHTS HOUSE	5066-0	Ceramic	NO	✓	RETIRED 1988	33.00	90.00

THE ORIGINAL SNOW VILLAGE

SV86-9

RAMSEY HILL HOUSE

Victorian with double chimneys. Steps to front door, porch is adjacent to entry. Side door also features small porch. Low balustrade fronts second story windows. Handpainting adds detailing to design.

SV86-10

SAINT JAMES CHURCH

Long central nave flanked by lower roofed side sections fronted by two towers. Gold main cross reinforced by smaller crosses on each section of tower roof. Smaller round windows repeat central window over entry. Announcement panels copy shape and design of front doors.

SV86-11

ALL SAINTS CHURCH

Smaller country church, simple design of long nave with entry door in base of bell tower.

SV86-12

CARRIAGE HOUSE

Small home from building used originally for carriages. A second story is achieved with many dormer windows changing the distinctive flat and curved roof. Fieldstone makes up the foundation allowing great weight during original function.

SV86-13

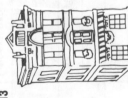

TOY SHOP

Front windows display toys. Roof molding brings focus to teddy bear design under pediment. Three story brick.

SV86-14

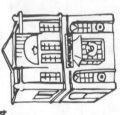

APOTHECARY

Two doors flank a central display bow window. Bas-relief of a mortar and pestle symbolizes the profession of owner and is on front panel above second floor family windows.

SV86-15

BAKERY

Corner bakery with two large multi-paned display windows protected by ribbed canopy. Greek key designs around roof edging highlight the bas-relief cupcake topped by a cherry that is centrally placed over entry.

SV86-16

DINER

An eating place based on the railroads famous dining car. Reputation of good, wholesome food. Large windows are a feature. Glass block entry protects diners from weather as customers come in/go out. Diners generally have counter service as well as a dining room.

ART CHART #	NAME	ITEM #	MATERIAL	SET?	🔔	MARKET STATUS	ORIGINAL SRP	GREENBOOK MKT PRICE
	VARIATIONS/MISC/COLLECTOR NOTES							
SV86-9	RAMSEY HILL HOUSE	5067-9	Ceramic	NO	✓	RETIRED 1989	$ 36.00	$ 96.00
	Early release to Gift Creations Concepts, Fall 1986.							
SV86-10	SAINT JAMES CHURCH	5068-7	Ceramic	NO	✓	RETIRED 1988	37.00	140.00
SV86-11	ALL SAINTS CHURCH	5070-9	Ceramic	NO	✓	CURRENT	38.00	45.00
SV86-12	CARRIAGE HOUSE	5071-7	Ceramic	NO	✓	RETIRED 1988	29.00	110.00
SV86-13	TOY SHOP	5073-3	Ceramic	NO	✓	RETIRED 1990	36.00	100.00
	Main Street design.							
SV86-14	APOTHECARY	5076-8	Ceramic	NO	✓	RETIRED 1990	34.00	92.00
	Main Street design.							
SV86-15	BAKERY	5077-6	Ceramic	NO	✓	RETIRED 1991	35.00	80.00
	Main Street design. Same Item # was used for the first Original Snow Village Bakery: 1981 Bakery (SV81-5).							
SV86-16	DINER	5078-4	Ceramic	NO	✓	RETIRED 1987	22.00	420.00
	Also known as "Mickey's."							

42

THE ORIGINAL SNOW VILLAGE

SV87-1

ST. ANTHONY HOTEL & POST OFFICE

Three story red brick with green trim. Dated 1886, the address of this hotel is "56 Main Street." American flag flies outside the ground floor P.O. Two chimneys and skylight on roof.

SV87-2

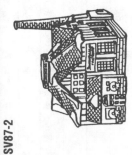

SNOW VILLAGE FACTORY

Wood building rises on stone block base with tall smokestack at rear. Factory products were available in small shop at front.

SV87-3

CATHEDRAL

Mosaic "stained glass" decorates the Gothic windows on all sides as well as the large turret.

SV87-4

CUMBERLAND HOUSE

Multi-colored curved roof supported by four columns, two chimneys, shuttered windows.

SV87-5

SPRINGFIELD HOUSE

Lower level has two multi-paned bay windows, one is bowed. Upper level windows are shuttered. Roof dormers are half-circle sunbursts. Stone chimney completes this clapboard home.

SV87-6

LIGHTHOUSE

Five story lighthouse beacon rises from sturdy stone slab base and is connected to caretaker's cottage.

SV87-7

RED BARN

Stone base, wooden barn, double cross-buck doors on long side, hayloft doors above main doors. Three ventilator cupolas on roof ridge. Cat sleeps in hayloft.

SV87-8

JEFFERSON SCHOOL

Two room schoolhouse with large multi-paned windows with top transoms. Short bell tower incorporated into roof.

ART CHART #	NAME	ITEM #	MATERIAL	SET?	♦∎	MARKET STATUS	ORIGINAL SRP	GREENBOOK MKT PRICE
	VARIATIONS/MISC/COLLECTOR NOTES							
SV87-1	ST. ANTHONY HOTEL & POST OFFICE	5006-7	Ceramic*	NO	✓	RETIRED 1989	$ 40.00	$ 100.00
	Main Street addition. *Metal flag.							
SV87-2	SNOW VILLAGE FACTORY	5013-0	Ceramic	SET OF 2	✓	RETIRED 1989	45.00	105.00
	Smoke stack is separate.							
SV87-3	CATHEDRAL	5019-9	Ceramic	NO	✓	RETIRED 1990	50.00	110.00
SV87-4	CUMBERLAND HOUSE	5024-5	Ceramic	NO	✓	CURRENT	42.00	44.00
SV87-5	SPRINGFIELD HOUSE	5027-0	Ceramic	NO	✓	RETIRED 1990	40.00	100.00
SV87-6	LIGHTHOUSE	5030-0	Ceramic	NO	✓	RETIRED 1988	36.00	340.00
SV87-7	RED BARN	5081-4	Ceramic	NO	✓	CURRENT	38.00	42.00
	Same Item # was used for the 1982 Gabled House (SV82-8). Early release to Gift Creations Concepts.							
SV87-8	JEFFERSON SCHOOL	5082-2	Ceramic	NO	✓	RETIRED 1991	36.00	90.00
	Same Item # was used for the 1982 Flower Shop (SV82-9). Early release to Gift Creations Concepts.							

THE ORIGINAL SNOW VILLAGE

SV87-9

FARM HOUSE
2 1/2 story wood frame home with front full-length porch. Roof interest is two low, one high peak with attic window in highest peak.

SV87-10

FIRE STATION NO. 2
Large double doors for station housing two engines, side stair leads to living quarters. Brick building with stone arch design at engine doors and front windows.

SV87-11

SNOW VILLAGE RESORT LODGE
Bright yellow with green, scalloped roof, covered porch and side entry. Bay windows on front house section. Back section rises to dormered 3 1/2 stories with louvered ventilator areas directly under roof cap.

ART CHART #	NAME	ITEM #	MATERIAL	SET?	🔔	MARKET STATUS	ORIGINAL SRP	GREENBOOK MKT PRICE
		VARIATIONS/MISC/COLLECTOR NOTES						
SV87-9	FARM HOUSE	5089-0	Ceramic	NO	✔	CURRENT	$ 40.00	$ 45.00
SV87-10	FIRE STATION NO. 2	5091-1	Ceramic	NO	✔	RETIRED 1989	40.00	120.00
	Early release to Gift Creations Concepts.							
SV87-11	SNOW VILLAGE RESORT LODGE	5092-0	Ceramic	NO	✔	RETIRED 1989	55.00	120.00

CLIPBOARD
• Effort to bring the accessories down to scale.

46

SV88-1

VILLAGE MARKET
Silk-screened "glass" windows detail merchandise available, red and white canopy protects shoppers using in/out doors. Sign over second story windows.

SV88-2

KENWOOD HOUSE
Old-fashioned wrap-around veranda with arched openings on three story home. Front facade features scalloped shingles on third story.

SV88-3

MAPLE RIDGE INN
Replica of Victorian mansion, ornamental roof piece concealed lightning rods.

SV88-4

VILLAGE STATION AND TRAIN
Station features an outside ticket window, soft drink vending machine, and outside benches, with a three car train.

SV88-5

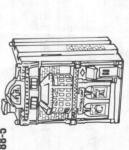

COBBLESTONE ANTIQUE SHOP
Silk-screened front windows display antiques for sale, bay window fills second story width, building date of 1881 on arched cornice.

SV88-6

CORNER CAFE
"Pie" and "Coffee" silkscreen on windows of corner restaurant with red, white, and blue striped awnings on main windows. Corner double door entrance. Building date of 1875 inscribed on corner turret design.

SV88-7

SINGLE CAR GARAGE
Double doors open to house car, two outside lights for convenience, designed to look like house, windows have shutters, roof has dormers, roof projects over wood pile.

SV88-8

HOME SWEET HOME/
HOUSE & WINDMILL
Based on landmark historic home, saltbox with asymmetrical arrangement of windows. Doors for root cellar are at front corner, one central brick chimney. Four bladed windmill.

ART CHART #	NAME	ITEM #	MATERIAL	SET?	☝	MARKET STATUS	ORIGINAL SRP	GREENBOOK MKT PRICE
	VARIATIONS/MISC/COLLECTOR NOTES							
SV88-1	VILLAGE MARKET	5044-0	Ceramic	NO	✓	RETIRED 1991	$ 39.00	$ 85.00
	Early release to Gift Creations Concepts.							
SV88-2	KENWOOD HOUSE	5054-7	Ceramic	NO	✓	RETIRED 1990	50.00	105.00
	Early release to Gift Creations Concepts.							
SV88-3	MAPLE RIDGE INN	5121-7	Ceramic	NO	✓	RETIRED 1990	55.00	98.00
	Interpretation of an American landmark in upstate New York.							
SV88-4	VILLAGE STATION AND TRAIN	5122-5	Ceramic	SET OF 4	✓	CURRENT	65.00	70.00
	Third Original Snow Village train and station design.							
SV88-5	COBBLESTONE ANTIQUE SHOP	5123-3	Ceramic	NO	✓	CURRENT	36.00	37.50
SV88-6	CORNER CAFE	5124-1	Ceramic	NO	✓	RETIRED 1991	37.00	75.00
SV88-7	SINGLE CAR GARAGE	5125-0	Ceramic	NO	✓	RETIRED 1990	22.00	50.00
SV88-8	HOME SWEET HOME/HOUSE & WINDMILL	5126-8	Ceramic	SET OF 2	✓	RETIRED 1991	60.00	105.00

48

SV88-9

REDEEMER CHURCH
Stone corners add strength and support to church and bell tower. Arched windows, heavy wooden double doors.

SV88-10

SERVICE STATION
Two gas pumps, candy machine, restroom, work area and office. White building blue roof, red trim.

SV88-11

STONEHURST HOUSE
Red brick punctuated with black and white painted bricks. Half circle sunburst design second story dormers restate the arch shape of first floor windows. Shutters repeat arch design.

SV88-12

PALOS VERDES
Spanish style with green tiled roof, covered entry porch, stucco finish, second floor has shuttered windows. Coming forward from main wing is two story round turret and ground floor window alcove.

ART CHART #	NAME	ITEM #	MATERIAL	SET?	![]	MARKET STATUS	ORIGINAL SRP	GREENBOOK MKT PRICE
	VARIATIONS/MISC/COLLECTOR NOTES							
SV88-9	REDEEMER CHURCH	5127-6	Ceramic	NO	✓	CURRENT	$ 42.00	$ 45.00
SV88-10	SERVICE STATION	5128-4	Ceramic	SET OF 2	✓	RETIRED 1991	37.50	90.00
	Pumps included.							
SV88-11	STONEHURST HOUSE	5140-3	Ceramic	NO	✓	CURRENT	37.50	37.50
SV88-12	PALOS VERDES	5141-1	Ceramic	NO	✓	RETIRED 1990	37.50	85.00
	Potted sisal miniature tree on porch - separate.							

THE ORIGINAL SNOW VILLAGE

SV89-1

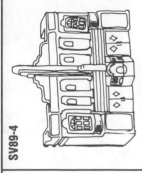

JINGLE BELLE HOUSEBOAT
Floating house sports a Christmas tree on wheelhouse roof and rear deck. Name is stenciled on bow and life preservers. Grey, blue, offset by red trim and white rails.

SV89-2

COLONIAL CHURCH
Front entry with four floor to roof columns supporting roof over porch. Front facade repeats design with four half columns set into wall. Circular windows ring upper part and are incorporated as upper half of side windows. Cross on three tier steeple bell tower.

SV89-3

NORTH CREEK COTTAGE
Cape cod style with colonial columned front porch. Attached garage with deck on top, front dormer, stone chimney.

SV89-4

PARAMOUNT THEATER
Spanish theme Art Deco building, double marques. Ticket booth in center flanked by two double doors. Corner billboards display scenes from movie.

SV89-5

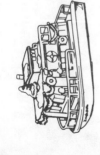

DOCTOR'S HOUSE
Home and office within house. Rounded turret completes front. Three story home has arched windows, porthole windows, and bay windows to add to Victorian charm. Yellow with light brown roof, white porch columns and molding decorate and highlight.

SV89-6

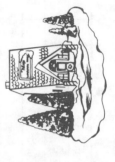

COURTHOUSE
Four corner roof turrets with central clock tower, windows with half circle sunbursts, decorative molding on second story with two front windows being clear half-circles for light. Greek key molding circles entire top. Basement visible via front windows.

SV89-7

VILLAGE WARMING HOUSE
Used by skaters to warm up from the chill, small red house has steep front roof. Bench at side for a brief rest.

SV89-8

J. YOUNG'S GRANARY
Central waterwheel for grinding grain, stone silo on one side, and small storage/store on other side.

ART CHART #	NAME	ITEM #	MATERIAL	SET?	!	MARKET STATUS	ORIGINAL SRP	GREENBOOK MKT PRICE
	VARIATIONS/MISC/COLLECTOR NOTES							
SV89-1	JINGLE BELLE HOUSEBOAT	5114-4	Ceramic	NO	✓	RETIRED 1991	$ 42.00	$ 90.00
SV89-2	COLONIAL CHURCH	5119-5	Ceramic*	NO	✓	CURRENT	60.00	60.00
	Early release to Gift Creations Concepts. *Metal cross.							
SV89-3	NORTH CREEK COTTAGE	5120-9	Ceramic	NO	✓	CURRENT	45.00	45.00
	Early release to Gift Creations Concepts.							
SV89-4	PARAMOUNT THEATER	5142-0	Ceramic	NO	✓	CURRENT	42.00	42.00
SV89-5	DOCTOR'S HOUSE	5143-8	Ceramic	NO	✓	CURRENT	56.00	56.00
SV89-6	COURTHOUSE	5144-6	Ceramic	NO	✓	CURRENT	65.00	65.00
SV89-7	VILLAGE WARMING HOUSE	5145-4	Ceramic	NO	✓	CURRENT	42.00	42.00
	Trees detach.							
SV89-8	J. YOUNG'S GRANARY	5149-7	Ceramic	NO	✓	CURRENT	45.00	45.00

SV89-9

PINEWOOD LOG CABIN
Log construction with two fireplaces for
heating/cooking, tree trunk porch pillars,
firewood stack, bucket for water, red roof,
house name on sign above porch,
attached tree.

ART CHART #	NAME	ITEM #	MATERIAL	SET?	☺	MARKET STATUS	ORIGINAL SRP	GREENBOOK MKT PRICE
SV89-9	PINEWOOD LOG CABIN	5150-0	Ceramic	NO	✓	CURRENT	$ 37.50	$ 37.50
	VARIATIONS/MISC/COLLECTOR NOTES							
	Early release to Gift Creations Concepts, Fall 1990.							

THE ORIGINAL SNOW VILLAGE

SV90-1

56 FLAVORS ICE CREAM PARLOR

Decorated like a sundae, peppermint pillars flank door, sugar cone roof with a cherry on peak, window boxes hold ice cream cones.

SV90-2

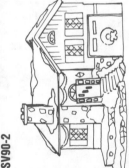

MORNINGSIDE HOUSE

Pink/coral split level house with one car garage. Fieldstone chimney, curved front steps, terraced landscaping with movable trees.

SV90-3

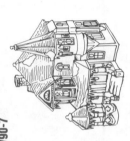

MAINSTREET HARDWARE STORE

Three story building with store on ground level. Rental rooms on second and third story with access by outside staircase. Awning covers store display window and front rooms on second floor.

SV90-4

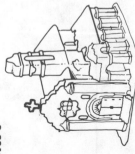

VILLAGE REALTY

Two story main building houses real estate office. Front bay display window for available properties. Shutters that follow curve of second story windows can open/close. Adjacent building houses small Italian dining place with colorful striped awning.

SV90-5

SPANISH MISSION CHURCH

Sun dried clay Spanish style, arcade along one side gives protected access.

SV90-6

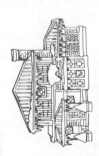

PRAIRIE HOUSE

Two story home with upper floor set in and back atop first story. Large windows to maximize light. Balcony area off one upper room. Large chimney rises up through first story. Two large pillars support covered entry.

SV90-7

QUEEN ANNE VICTORIAN

Broad steps lead up to pillared porch with unique corner gazebo style sitting area. Ornate turret on corner of second story decorated with scalloped shingles.

ART CHART #	NAME	ITEM #	MATERIAL	SET?	♻	MARKET STATUS	ORIGINAL SRP	GREENBOOK MKT PRICE
	VARIATIONS/MISC/COLLECTOR NOTES							
SV90-1	56 FLAVORS ICE CREAM PARLOR	5151-9	Ceramic	NO	✓	CURRENT	$ 42.00	$ 45.00
	Early release to Gift Creations Concepts.							
SV90-2	MORNINGSIDE HOUSE	5152-7	Ceramic	NO	✓	CURRENT	45.00	45.00
	Early release to Showcase Dealers and the National Association of Limited Edition Dealers.							
SV90-3	MAINSTREET HARDWARE STORE	5153-5	Ceramic	NO	✓	CURRENT	42.00	42.00
SV90-4	VILLAGE REALTY	5154-3	Ceramic	NO	✓	CURRENT	42.00	42.00
SV90-5	SPANISH MISSION CHURCH	5155-1	Ceramic	NO	✓	CURRENT	42.00	42.00
SV90-6	PRAIRIE HOUSE	5156-0	Ceramic	NO	✓	CURRENT	42.00	42.00
	American Architecture Series.							
SV90-7	QUEEN ANNE VICTORIAN	5157-8	Ceramic	NO	✓	CURRENT	48.00	48.00
	American Architecture Series.							

SV91-1

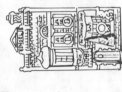

THE CHRISTMAS SHOP
Pediment on brick building advertises
the holiday by the French "NOEL."
Striped awning over door.
Large Teddy Bear by front window.

SV91-2

OAK GROVE TUDOR
Red brick base with stucco and
timbered second story.
Fireplace of brick and stone by entry door.
Rough stone frames door.
Bay window with flower boxes.

SV91-3

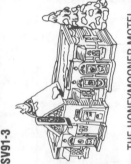

THE HONEYMOONER MOTEL
Moon and stars sign above office door
is advertisement for motel.
White building with blue awnings & doors.
Windows and trim in red.
Soda and ice machine by office door.

SV91-4

VILLAGE GREENHOUSE
Plant growing area has bricked bottom
and "glass" roof to allow sunlight in.
Attached small store sells accessories.
It has brick chimney, shingled roof,
and covered entry.

SV91-5

SOUTHERN COLONIAL
Four columns rise from ground to roof with second story veranda across front.
Double chimneys surrounded by a balustrade. Shutters by each window both
decorate and shut out heat of sun. Two urns flank steps of entryway.

SV91-6

GOTHIC FARMHOUSE
Columned front porch and entry. First floor large bay window with second story rising
to a gable with carved molding which is repeated on two dormer windows over porch.
Clapboard home with roof shingles in diamond pattern.

ART CHART #	NAME	ITEM #	MATERIAL	SET?	🔔	MARKET STATUS	ORIGINAL SRP	GREENBOOK MKT PRICE
	VARIATIONS/MISC/COLLECTOR NOTES							
SV91-1	THE CHRISTMAS SHOP	5097-0	Ceramic	NO	✓	CURRENT	$ 37.50	$ 37.50
	Early release to Gift Creations Concepts and Showcase Dealers.							
SV91-2	OAK GROVE TUDOR	5400-3	Ceramic	NO	✓	CURRENT	42.00	42.00
	Early release to Showcase Dealers.							
SV91-3	THE HONEYMOONER MOTEL	5401-1	Ceramic	NO	✓	CURRENT	42.00	42.00
	Early release to Showcase Dealers.							
SV91-4	VILLAGE GREENHOUSE	5402-0	Ceramic*	NO	✓	CURRENT	35.00	35.00
	* Acrylic panels.							
SV91-5	SOUTHERN COLONIAL	5403-8	Ceramic	NO	✓	CURRENT	48.00	48.00
	American Architecture Series.							
SV91-6	GOTHIC FARMHOUSE	5404-6	Ceramic	NO	✓	CURRENT	48.00	48.00
	American Architecture Series.							

58

SV91-7

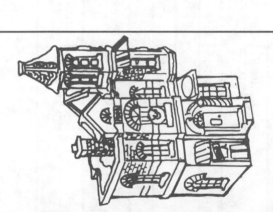

FINKLEA'S FINERY COSTUME SHOP
Pediment over front door repeated in roof design. Red awnings over 1st floor display windows. Dressed stone trims the facade of the three story brick building. Hood projects over third floor windows - an area used by piano teacher. Attached side setback is two storys with decorated rental return door and awning on upper window.

SV91-8

JACK'S CORNER BARBER SHOP
Also houses M. Schmitt Photography Studio and second floor Tailor Shop. Two story turret separates two identical wings of brick building. Fantail window design repeated on doors and on roof peaks.

SV91-9

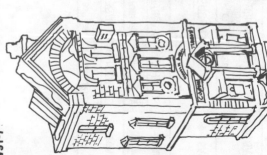

DOUBLE BUNGALOW
Early two family home - double entry doors, each side has bow window downstairs, a roof dormer, and own chimney. A brick facade dresses up clapboard house.

ART CHART #	NAME	ITEM #	MATERIAL	SET?	♦	MARKET STATUS	ORIGINAL SRP	GREENBOOK MKT PRICE
			VARIATIONS/MISC/COLLECTOR NOTES					
SV91-7	FINKLEA'S FINERY COSTUME SHOP	5405-4	Ceramic	NO	✓	CURRENT	$ 45.00	$ 45.00
SV91-8	JACK'S CORNER BARBER SHOP	5406-2	Ceramic	NO	✓	CURRENT	42.00	42.00
SV91-9	DOUBLE BUNGALOW	5407-0	Ceramic	NO	✓	CURRENT	45.00	45.00

THE ORIGINAL SNOW VILLAGE

SV92-2

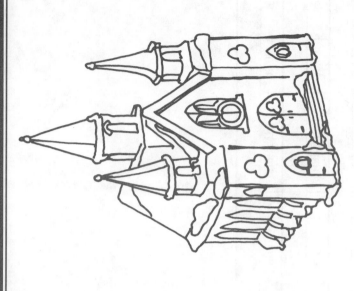

ST. LUKE'S CHURCH

Brick church features three square based steeples with the central one rising off nave roof. Other two are front corners of church with doors at base and trefoil design on the front/side repeated on main entry doors. Ribbing on side walls between tall, narrow windows.

SV92-1

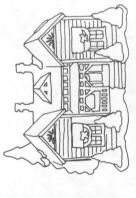

GRANDMA'S HOUSE

Small porch nestled between two identical house sections. Hooded double windows, front side sections with evergreens flanking each area. Double chimneys rise off main roof. White clapboard with carved fan-like design on each gable.

SV92-3

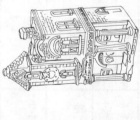

POST OFFICE

Doric columns support porch to double entry doors. Two story brick with two story turret rising above sign. Greek key and incised design separate stories. Door and windows repeat arched design. Molding accents roof.

ART CHART #	NAME	ITEM #	MATERIAL	SET?	✋	MARKET STATUS	ORIGINAL SRP	GREENBOOK MKT PRICE
	VARIATIONS/MISC/COLLECTOR NOTES							
SV92-1	GRANDMA'S HOUSE	5420-8	Ceramic	NO	✓	CURRENT	$ 42.00	$ 42.00
	Early release to Gift Creations Concepts.							
SV92-2	ST. LUKE'S CHURCH	5421-6	Ceramic	NO	✓	CURRENT	45.00	45.00
	Early release to Gift Creations Concepts.							
SV92-3	POST OFFICE	5422-4	Ceramic	NO	✓	CURRENT	35.00	35.00
	Early release to Showcase Dealers.							

SVA79-1

CAROLERS
Couple, girl, garlanded
lamppost, snowman.

SVA80-2

CERAMIC CAR
Open roadster holds lap rugs,
Christmas tree, and wrapped presents.

SVA81-3

CERAMIC SLEIGH
Patterned after old fashioned
wood sleigh, holds Christmas tree
and wrapped presents.

SVA82-4

SNOWMAN WITH BROOM
Top hat, red nose,
snowman holds straw broom.

SVA83-5

MONKS-A-CAROLING
Four friars singing carols.

SVA84-6

SCOTTIE WITH TREE
Black dog waits by snow covered tree
with star at top.

SVA84-7

MONKS-A-CAROLING
Four friars singing carols.

SVA85-8

SINGING NUNS
Four nuns in habits, sing carols.

ART CHART #	NAME	ITEM #	MATERIAL	SET?	💡	MARKET STATUS	ORIGINAL SRP	GREENBOOK MKT PRICE
	VARIATIONS/MISC/COLLECTOR NOTES							
SVA79-1	CAROLERS (1979)	5064-1	Ceramic	SET OF 4		RETIRED 1986	$ 12.00	$ 105.00
	First non-lit accessory.							
SVA80-2	CERAMIC CAR (1980)	5069-0	Ceramic	NO		RETIRED 1986	5.00	42.00
	First vehicle, no other cars available until 1985.							
SVA81-3	CERAMIC SLEIGH (1981)	5079-2	Ceramic	NO		RETIRED 1986	5.00	52.00
SVA82-4	SNOWMAN WITH BROOM (1982)	5018-0	Ceramic	NO		RETIRED 1990	3.00	15.00
SVA83-5	MONKS-A-CAROLING (1983)	6459-9	Ceramic	NO		RETIRED 1984	6.00	70.00
	Retired after just one year due to maker being unable to supply. Re-introduced in 1984 as #5040-7 (SVA84-7) from another supplier. See page 225.							
SVA84-6	SCOTTIE WITH TREE (1984)	5038-5	Ceramic	NO		RETIRED 1985	3.00	115.00
SVA84-7	MONKS-A-CAROLING (1984)	5040-7	Ceramic	NO		RETIRED 1988	6.00	25.00
	Replaced 1983 Monks-A-Caroling #6459-9 (SVA83-5). See page 225.							
SVA85-8	SINGING NUNS (1985)	5053-9	Ceramic	NO		RETIRED 1987	6.00	75.00

SVA85-9

AUTO WITH TREE
Red VW Beetle with tree strapped to roof.

SVA85-10

SNOW KIDS SLED, SKIS
Three children on a toboggan
and one child on skis.

SVA85-11

FAMILY MOM/KIDS, GOOSE/GIRL
Mother holds hands of two children,
one girl feeds corn to geese.

SVA85-12

SANTA/MAILBOX
Santa with toy bag.
Girl mails letter to Santa as dog watches.

SVA86-13

KIDS AROUND THE TREE
Children join hands to make a ring around
the snow covered tree with a gold star.

SVA86-14

GIRL/SNOWMAN, BOY
Girl puts finishing touches on
snowman as boy reaches to place
decorated hat atop head.

SVA86-15

SHOPPING GIRLS WITH PACKAGES
Girls dressed toasty for shopping with
hats, mittens, coats, boots, stand by
some of their wrapped packages.

SVA87-16

WHITE PICKET FENCE
White metal decorative fence usually
used at a private home or to define a
formal garden.

ART CHART #	NAME	ITEM #	MATERIAL	SET?	♪ MARKET STATUS	ORIGINAL SRP	GREENBOOK MKT PRICE
	VARIATIONS/MISC/COLLECTOR NOTES						
SVA85-9	AUTO WITH TREE (1985)	5055-5	Ceramic/Sisal	NO	CURRENT	$ 5.00	$ 6.50
SVA85-10	SNOW KIDS SLED, SKIS (1985)	5056-3	Ceramic	SET OF 2	RETIRED 1987	11.00	48.00
SVA85-11	FAMILY MOM/KIDS, GOOSE/GIRL (1985)	5057-1	Ceramic	SET OF 2	RETIRED 1988	11.00	35.00
SVA85-12	SANTA/MAILBOX (1985)	5059-8	Ceramic	SET OF 2	RETIRED 1988	11.00	40.00
SVA86-13	KIDS AROUND THE TREE (1986)	5094-6	Ceramic	NO	RETIRED 1990	15.00	32.00
	Variations in size. GREENBOOK Market Price for larger, pre-1987 size, is $60.00.						
SVA86-14	GIRL/SNOWMAN, BOY (1986)	5095-4	Ceramic	SET OF 2	RETIRED 1987	11.00	50.00
SVA86-15	SHOPPING GIRLS WITH PACKAGES (1986)	5096-2	Ceramic	SET OF 2	RETIRED 1988	11.00	35.00
	Variations in size, pre-1987 size is larger.						
SVA87-16	WHITE PICKET FENCE (1987)	5100-4	Metal	NO	CURRENT	3.00	3.00
	Size is 6" x 1.75". One of the first metal accessories (other was Park Bench). Also available in a set of 4, Item #5101-2, @ $12.00 SRP.						

SVA87-20

CAROLING FAMILY
Father holds baby, mother and son, and girl with pup.

SVA87-24

VILLAGE PARK BENCH
Green metal bench usually found on a Village Green, park, or at a public building.

SVA87-19

CHILDREN IN BAND
One child conducts three band players: horn, drum, and tuba.

SVA87-23

FOR SALE SIGN
Holly decorates a house for sale sign. Usually sign post inserted at edge of property to be seen by drivers and people passing by.

SVA87-18

PRAYING MONKS
Three monks, standing side-by-side, praying.

SVA87-22

CHRISTMAS CHILDREN
Children at outdoor activities: girl and pup on sled pulled by boy, girl holding wreath, girl feeding carrot to bunny.

SVA87-17

3 NUNS WITH SONGBOOKS
Three nuns in habits carry songbooks to sing carols.

SVA87-21

TAXI CAB
Yellow Checker cab.

ART CHART #	NAME	ITEM #	MATERIAL	SET?	💰	MARKET STATUS	ORIGINAL SRP	GREENBOOK MKT PRICE
	VARIATIONS/MISC/COLLECTOR NOTES							
SVA87-17	3 NUNS WITH SONGBOOKS (1987)	5102-0	Ceramic	NO		RETIRED 1988	$ 6.00	$ 75.00
SVA87-18	PRAYING MONKS (1987)	5103-9	Ceramic	NO		RETIRED 1988	6.00	32.00
SVA87-19	CHILDREN IN BAND (1987)	5104-7	Ceramic	NO		RETIRED 1989	15.00	35.00
SVA87-20	CAROLING FAMILY (1987)	5105-5	Ceramic	SET OF 3		RETIRED 1990	20.00	35.00
SVA87-21	TAXI CAB (1987)	5106-3	Ceramic	NO		CURRENT	6.00	6.50
SVA87-22	CHRISTMAS CHILDREN (1987)	5107-1	Ceramic	SET OF 4		RETIRED 1990	20.00	35.00
SVA87-23	FOR SALE SIGN (1987)	5108-0	Ceramic	NO		RETIRED 1989	3.50	12.00
	Variation: Blank sign for personalization, #581-9, Gift Creations Concepts 1989 Christmas Catalog Exclusive, free w/$100 Dept. 56 purchase.							
SVA87-24	VILLAGE PARK BENCH (1987)	5109-8	Metal	NO		CURRENT	3.00	3.20
	Size is 2.5". One of the first metal accessories (other was Picket Fence). Also considered to be a Heritage Village Accessory.							

SVA87-25

SNOW KIDS
Three kids on toboggan, child on skis, boy and girl putting finishing touches on snowman.

SVA88-26

VILLAGE TOWN CLOCK
Free standing large faced clock on a pedestal base usually on display on a business street, train station, or public building.

SVA88-27

MAN ON LADDER HANGING GARLAND
Man carries garland up ladder to decorate eaves of house.

SVA88-28

HAYRIDE
Farmer guides horse-drawn hay-filled sleigh with children as riders.

SVA88-29

SCHOOL CHILDREN
Three children carrying school books.

SVA88-30

APPLE GIRL/NEWSPAPER BOY
Girl holds wood tray carrier selling apples for 5¢, newsboy sells the Village News.

SVA88-31

WOODSMAN AND BOY
Man chops and splits logs and boy prepares to carry supply to fireplace.

SVA88-32

DOGHOUSE/CAT IN GARBAGE CAN
Dog sits outside doghouse decorated with wreath; cat looks at empty boxes and wrappings in garbage can.

ART CHART #	NAME	ITEM #	MATERIAL	SET?		MARKET STATUS	ORIGINAL SRP	GREENBOOK MKT PRICE
SVA87-25	SNOW KIDS (1987)	5113-6	Ceramic	SET OF 4		RETIRED 1990	$ 20.00	$ 52.00
	VARIATIONS/MISC/COLLECTOR NOTES							
	Set of 4 incorporates 1985 #5056-3 (SVA85-10) and 1986 #5095-4 (SVA86-14), re-scaled to the smaller size.							
SVA88-26	VILLAGE TOWN CLOCK (1988)	5110-1	Metal	NO		CURRENT	2.70	2.80
	Size is 3.5". Choice of green or black. Also considered to be a Heritage Village Accessory.							
SVA88-27	MAN ON LADDER HANGING GARLAND (1988)	5116-0	See Below	NO		CURRENT	7.50	8.00
	Ladder is wooden, garland is fiber, man is ceramic.							
SVA88-28	HAYRIDE (1988)	5117-9	Ceramic	NO		RETIRED 1990	30.00	65.00
SVA88-29	SCHOOL CHILDREN (1988)	5118-7	Ceramic	SET OF 3		RETIRED 1990	15.00	30.00
SVA88-30	APPLE GIRL/NEWSPAPER BOY (1988)	5129-2	Ceramic	SET OF 2		RETIRED 1990	11.00	25.00
SVA88-31	WOODSMAN AND BOY (1988)	5130-6	Ceramic	SET OF 2		RETIRED 1991	13.00	26.00
SVA88-32	DOGHOUSE/CAT IN GARBAGE CAN (1988)	5131-4	Ceramic	SET OF 2		CURRENT	15.00	15.00

SVA88-33

FIRE HYDRANT AND MAILBOX
Red fire hydrant and rural curbside mailbox on post.

SVA88-34

WATER TOWER
Metal scaffold base holds red ceramic water container with green top, ladder leads to top.

SVA88-35

NATIVITY
Holy Family, lamb, in creche scene.

SVA88-36

WOODY STATION WAGON
"Wood" paneled sides on station wagon.

SVA88-37

SCHOOL BUS, SNOW PLOW
Yellow school bus and red sand gravel truck with snow plow.

SVA88-38

TREE LOT
Christmas lights on tree lot's fence plus decorated shack and trees for sale.

SVA88-39

UP ON A ROOF TOP
Santa and sleigh pulled by eight reindeer.

SVA88-40

SISAL TREE LOT
A variety of cut trees for sale at a street lot.

ART CHART #	NAME	ITEM #	MATERIAL	SET?	🚻	MARKET STATUS	ORIGINAL SRP	GREENBOOK MKT PRICE
	VARIATIONS/MISC/COLLECTOR NOTES							
SVA88-33	FIRE HYDRANT AND MAILBOX (1988)	5132-2	Metal	SET OF 2		CURRENT	$ 6.00	$ 6.00
	Sizes are 1.5" and 2.75", respectively.							
SVA88-34	WATER TOWER (1988)	5133-0	Metal/Ceramic	2 PIECES		RETIRED 1991	20.00	48.00
	"John Deere Co." Water Tower (1989), #2510-4, Original SRP was $24.00 + Shipping. GREENBOOK Market Price is $125.00.							
SVA88-35	NATIVITY (1988)	5135-7	Ceramic	NO		CURRENT	7.50	7.50
SVA88-36	WOODY STATION WAGON (1988)	5136-5	Ceramic	NO		RETIRED 1990	6.50	20.00
SVA88-37	SCHOOL BUS, SNOW PLOW (1988)	5137-3	Ceramic	SET OF 2		RETIRED 1991	16.00	25.00
SVA88-38	TREE LOT (1988)	5138-1	See Below	NO		CURRENT	33.50	37.50
	Sisal trees, wood fence, ceramic shack.							
SVA88-39	UP ON A ROOF TOP (1988)	5139-0	Pewter	2 PIECES		CURRENT	6.50	6.50
	Size is 4" long. Also considered to be a Heritage Village Accessory.							
SVA88-40	SISAL TREE LOT (1988)	8183-3	Sisal	NO		RETIRED 1991	45.00	80.00

SVA89-41

VILLAGE GAZEBO
Small, open, red roofed garden structure that will protect folks from rain/snow, or be a private place to sit.

SVA89-42

CHOIR KIDS
Four kids in white and red robes with green songbooks caroling.

SVA89-43

SPECIAL DELIVERY
Mailman and mailbag with his mail truck in USPO colors red, white, and blue with the eagle logo.

SVA89-44

FOR SALE SIGN
Enameled metal sign can be "For Sale" or "SOLD." Birds decorate and add color.

SVA89-45

STREET SIGN
Green street signs can be personalized to give each village street a unique name.

SVA89-46

KIDS TREE HOUSE
Decorated club house built on an old dead tree. Steps lead up to hideaway.

SVA89-47

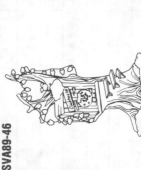

BRINGING HOME THE TREE
Man pulls sled holding tree as girl watches to make sure it doesn't fall off.

SVA89-48

SKATE FASTER MOM
Two children sit in sleigh as skating Mom pushes them across the ice.

ART CHART #	NAME	ITEM #	MATERIAL	SET?	●	MARKET STATUS	ORIGINAL SRP	GREENBOOK MKT PRICE
	VARIATIONS/MISC/COLLECTOR NOTES							
SVA89-41	VILLAGE GAZEBO (1989)	5146-2	Ceramic	NO		CURRENT	$ 27.00	$ 28.00
SVA89-42	CHOIR KIDS (1989)	5147-0	Ceramic	NO		CURRENT	15.00	15.00
SVA89-43	SPECIAL DELIVERY (1989)	5148-9	Ceramic	SET OF 2		RETIRED 1990	16.00	42.00
	Discontinued due to licensing problems with the U.S. Postal Service. Replaced with 1990 Special Delivery #5197-7 (SVA90-68).							
SVA89-44	FOR SALE SIGN (1989)	5166-7	Metal	NO		CURRENT	4.50	4.50
	Size is 3" tall.							
SVA89-45	STREET SIGN (1989)	5167-5	Metal	6 PCS/PKG		CURRENT	7.50	7.50
	Use street names provided (Lake St., Maple Dr., Park Ave., River Rd., Elm St., Ivy Lane.....) or personalize. Size is 4.25" tall.							
SVA89-46	KIDS TREE HOUSE (1989)	5168-3	Resin	NO		RETIRED 1991	25.00	48.00
SVA89-47	BRINGING HOME THE TREE (1989)	5169-1	Ceramic/Sisal	NO		CURRENT	15.00	15.00
SVA89-48	SKATE FASTER MOM (1989)	5170-5	Ceramic	NO		RETIRED 1991	13.00	30.00

... ACCESSORIES ... THE ORIGINAL SNOW VILLAGE ... ACCESSORIES ...

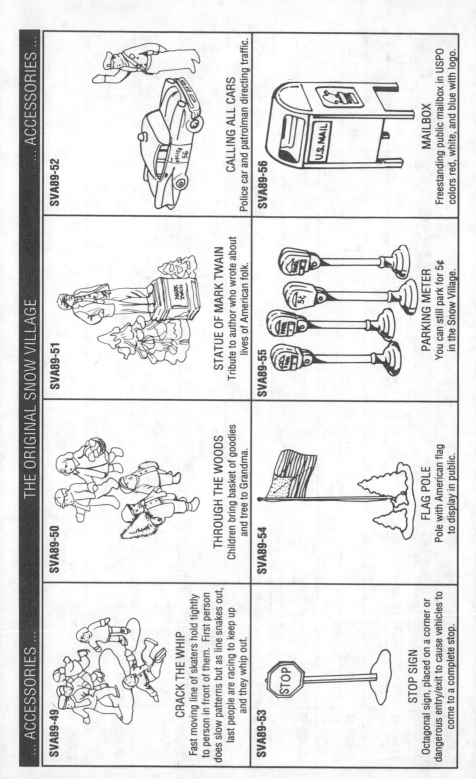

SVA89-49

CRACK THE WHIP
Fast moving line of skaters hold tightly to person in front of them. First person does slow patterns but as line snakes out, last people are racing to keep up and they whip out.

SVA89-50

THROUGH THE WOODS
Children bring basket of goodies and tree to Grandma.

SVA89-51

STATUE OF MARK TWAIN
Tribute to author who wrote about lives of American folk.

SVA89-52

CALLING ALL CARS
Police car and patrolman directing traffic.

SVA89-53

STOP SIGN
Octagonal sign, placed on a corner or dangerous entry/exit to cause vehicles to come to a complete stop.

SVA89-54

FLAG POLE
Pole with American flag to display in public.

SVA89-55

PARKING METER
You can still park for 5¢ in the Snow Village.

SVA89-56

MAILBOX
Freestanding public mailbox in USPO colors red, white, and blue with logo.

ART CHART #	NAME	ITEM #	MATERIAL	SET?	🖐	MARKET STATUS	ORIGINAL SRP	GREENBOOK MKT PRICE
	VARIATIONS/MISC/COLLECTOR NOTES							
SVA89-49	CRACK THE WHIP (1989)	5171-3	Ceramic	SET OF 3		CURRENT	$ 25.00	$ 25.00
SVA89-50	THROUGH THE WOODS (1989)	5172-1	Ceramic/Sisal	SET OF 2		RETIRED 1991	18.00	30.00
SVA89-51	STATUE OF MARK TWAIN (1989)	5173-0	Ceramic	NO		RETIRED 1991	15.00	28.00
SVA89-52	CALLING ALL CARS (1989)	5174-8	Ceramic	SET OF 2		RETIRED 1991	15.00	32.00
SVA89-53	STOP SIGN (1989)	5176-4	Metal	2 PCS/PKG		CURRENT	5.00	5.00
	Size is 3" tall.							
SVA89-54	FLAG POLE (1989)	5177-2	See Below	NO		CURRENT	8.50	8.50
	Resin base, metal pole, cloth flag, thread rope. Size is 7" tall.							
SVA89-55	PARKING METER (1989)	5178-0	Metal	4 PCS/PKG		CURRENT	6.00	6.00
	Size is 2" tall.							
SVA89-56	MAILBOX (1989)	5179-9	Metal	NO		RETIRED 1990	3.50	20.00
	Discontinued due to licensing problems with the U.S. Postal Service. Replaced with 1990 Mailbox #5198-5 (SVA90-69).							

THE ORIGINAL SNOW VILLAGE

SVA89-57

VILLAGE BIRDS
Small red and blue sitting birds for use in decorating and as accessories.

SVA89-58

VILLAGE POTTED TOPIARY PAIR
Sisal evergreen trees in large planters, pruned in size and shape for formal garden and/or display.

SVA90-59

KIDS DECORATING
THE VILLAGE SIGN
Two children place garland on Snow Village Sign.

SVA90-60

DOWN THE CHIMNEY HE GOES
Santa with bag of toys enters chimney to make delivery on Christmas Eve.

SVA90-61

SNO-JET SNOWMOBILE
Snowmobile, red with silver trim, front ski runners and rear caterpillar treads.

SVA90-62

SLEIGHRIDE
Family rides in open old fashioned green sleigh pulled by one horse.

SVA90-63

HERE WE COME A CAROLING
Children and pet dog sing carols.

SVA90-64

HOME DELIVERY
Milkman and milk truck.

ART CHART #	NAME	ITEM #	MATERIAL	SET?	🔔	MARKET STATUS	ORIGINAL SRP	GREENBOOK MKT PRICE
	VARIATIONS/MISC/COLLECTOR NOTES							
SVA89-57	VILLAGE BIRDS (1989)	5180-2	Metal	6 PCS/PKG		CURRENT	$ 3.50	$ 3.50
	Also considered to be a Heritage Village Accessory.							
SVA89-58	VILLAGE POTTED TOPIARY PAIR (1989)	5192-6	Sisal/Resin	PAIR		CURRENT	5.00	5.00
	Size is 4.75' tall. Also considered to be a Heritage Village Accessory.							
SVA90-59	KIDS DECORATING THE VILLAGE SIGN (1990)	5134-9	Ceramic	NO		CURRENT	12.50	12.50
SVA90-60	DOWN THE CHIMNEY HE GOES (1990)	5158-6	Ceramic	NO		CURRENT	6.50	6.50
SVA90-61	SNO-JET SNOWMOBILE (1990)	5159-4	Ceramic	NO		CURRENT	15.00	15.00
SVA90-62	SLEIGHRIDE (1990)	5160-8	Ceramic	NO		CURRENT	30.00	30.00
SVA90-63	HERE WE COME A CAROLING (1990)	5161-6	Ceramic	SET OF 3		CURRENT	18.00	18.00
SVA90-64	HOME DELIVERY (1990)	5162-4	Ceramic	SET OF 2		CURRENT	16.00	16.00

SVA90-68

SPECIAL DELIVERY
Snow Village postman and truck in red and green Snow Village Mail Service colors.

SVA90-67

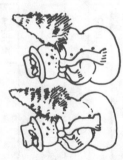

A HOME FOR THE HOLIDAYS
Red and yellow birdhouse on a pole with blue bird sitting on roof. Pole decorated with garland and small snow covered evergreen.

SVA90-66

A TREE FOR ME
Snowman with top hat, corn cob pipe, and red muffler carries his own small snow covered tree.

SVA90-65

FRESH FROZEN FISH
Ice Fisherman, Ice House

SVA91-72

WINTER FOUNTAIN
Angel holds sea shell with water frozen as it flowed.

SVA91-71

WREATHS FOR SALE
Girl holds for sale sign, boy holds up wreaths, child pulls sled to carry wreaths. Fence holds wreaths.

SVA90-70

CHRISTMAS TRASH CANS
Two galvanized refuse cans filled with holiday wrappings and garbage.

SVA90-69

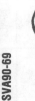

MAILBOX
Snow Village mail receptacle in red and green Snow Village Mail Service colors.

ART CHART #	NAME	ITEM #	MATERIAL	SET?	🔔	MARKET STATUS	ORIGINAL SRP	GREENBOOK MKT PRICE
	VARIATIONS/MISC/COLLECTOR NOTES							
SVA90-65	FRESH FROZEN FISH (1990)	5163-2	Ceramic	SET OF 2		CURRENT	$ 20.00	$ 20.00
SVA90-66	A TREE FOR ME (1990)	5164-0	Ceramic/Sisal	2 PCS/PKG		CURRENT	7.50	7.50
SVA90-67	A HOME FOR THE HOLIDAYS (1990)	5165-9	Ceramic	NO		CURRENT	6.50	6.50
SVA90-68	SPECIAL DELIVERY (1990)	5197-7	Ceramic	SET OF 2		CURRENT	16.00	16.00
	"S.V. Mail" Service. Replaces discontinued 1985 Special Delivery #5148-9 (SVA89-43).							
SVA90-69	MAILBOX (1990)	5198-5	Metal	NO		CURRENT	3.50	3.50
	Size is 2". "S.V. Mail" Service. Replaces discontinued 1985 Mailbox #5179-9 (SVA89-56).							
SVA90-70	CHRISTMAS TRASH CANS (1990)	5209-4	See Below	SET OF 2		CURRENT	6.50	7.00
	Size is 1.5". Metal/Plastic/Paper. Tops come off.							
SVA91-71	WREATHS FOR SALE (1991)	5408-9	See Below	SET OF 4		CURRENT	27.50	27.50
	Ceramic/Wood/Sisal.							
SVA91-72	WINTER FOUNTAIN (1991)	5409-7	See Below	NO		CURRENT	25.00	25.00
	Ceramic/Acrylic.							

... ACCESSORIES

THE ORIGINAL SNOW VILLAGE

... ACCESSORIES

SVA91-73

COLD WEATHER SPORTS
Three children play ice hockey.

SVA91-74

COME JOIN THE PARADE
Two children carry parade banner.

SVA91-75

VILLAGE MARCHING BAND
Drum Major, two horn players, and two drummers.

SVA91-76

CHRISTMAS CADILLAC
Pink car holds tree and presents.

SVA91-77

SNOWBALL FORT
One boy behind wall, one hides behind tree, one in open clearing - all with snowballs to throw.

SVA91-78

COUNTRY HARVEST
Farm folk with market basket and pitchfork. (Reminiscent of American Gothic painting...)

SVA91-79

VILLAGE GREETINGS
Holiday banners to hang on side of buildings.

ART CHART #	NAME	ITEM #	MATERIAL	SET?	⬥	MARKET STATUS	ORIGINAL SRP	GREENBOOK MKT PRICE
	VARIATIONS/MISC/COLLECTOR NOTES							
SVA91-73	COLD WEATHER SPORTS (1991)	5410-0	Ceramic	SET OF 4		CURRENT	$ 27.50	$ 27.50
SVA91-74	COME JOIN THE PARADE (1991)	5411-9	Ceramic	NO		CURRENT	12.50	12.50
SVA91-75	VILLAGE MARCHING BAND (1991)	5412-7	Ceramic	SET OF 3		CURRENT	30.00	30.00
SVA91-76	CHRISTMAS CADILLAC (1991)	5413-5	Ceramic/Sisal	NO		CURRENT	9.00	9.00
SVA91-77	SNOWBALL FORT (1991)	5414-3	Ceramic	SET OF 3		CURRENT	27.50	27.50
SVA91-78	COUNTRY HARVEST (1991)	5415-1	Ceramic	NO		CURRENT	13.00	13.00
SVA91-79	VILLAGE GREETINGS (1991)	5418-6	Metal	SET OF 3		CURRENT	5.00	5.00

MEADOWLAND

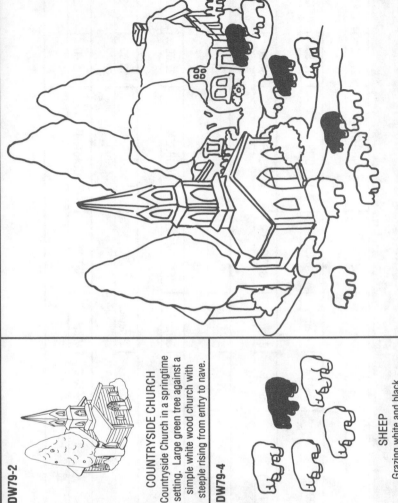

MEADOWLAND (COMPOSITE)

MDW79-1

THATCHED COTTAGE
Small thatched cottage with attached tree. Chimney at rear of stucco and timber trim.

MDW79-2

COUNTRYSIDE CHURCH
Countryside Church in a springtime setting. Large green tree against a simple white wood church with steeple rising from entry to nave.

MDW79-3

ASPEN TREES
The trees that shiver and tremble in the wind. Small leaves on a hardwood tree.

MDW79-4

SHEEP
Grazing white and black sheep make up this flock.

ART CHART #	NAME	ITEM #	MATERIAL	SET?	☎	MARKET STATUS	ORIGINAL SRP	GREENBOOK MKT PRICE
	VARIATIONS/MISC/COLLECTOR NOTES							
MDW79-1	THATCHED COTTAGE	5050-0	Ceramic	NO	✓	RETIRED 1980	$ 30.00	$ 600.00
MDW79-2	COUNTRYSIDE CHURCH	5051-8	Ceramic	NO	✓	RETIRED 1980	25.00	NE
	For snow version see 1979 Countryside Church #5058-3 (SV79-5).							
MDW79-3	ASPEN TREES (ACCESSORY)	5052-6	Ceramic	NO		RETIRED 1980	16.00	NE
MDW79-4	SHEEP (ACCESSORY)	5053-4	Ceramic	SET OF 12		RETIRED 1980	12.00	NE
	9 white, 3 black.							

CLIPBOARD
• Technically not part of the Original Snow Village. Limited distribution.

NE = NOT ESTABLISHED

84

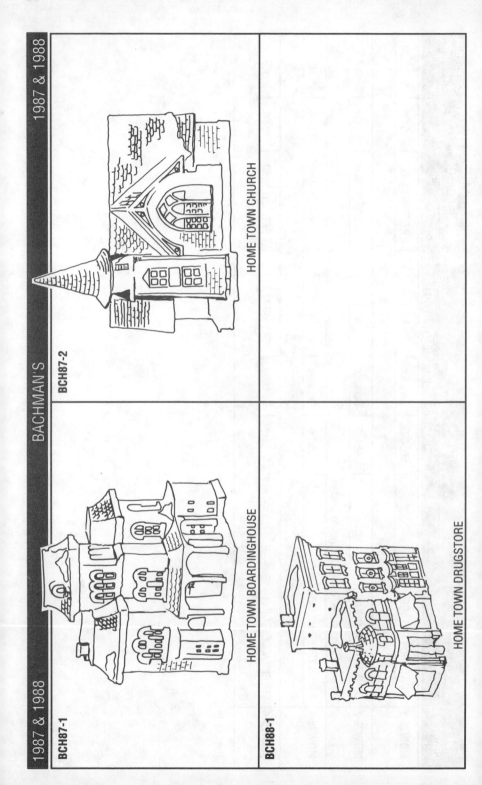

BACHMAN'S

1987 & 1988

BCH87-1
HOME TOWN BOARDINGHOUSE

BCH87-2
HOME TOWN CHURCH

BCH88-1
HOME TOWN DRUGSTORE

ART CHART #	NAME	ITEM #	MATERIAL	SET?	🔄	MARKET STATUS	ORIGINAL SRP	GREENBOOK MKT PRICE
	VARIATIONS/MISC/COLLECTOR NOTES							
BCH87-1	HOME TOWN BOARDING HOUSE (1987 - 1988)	670-0	Porcelain	NO	✓	DISCONTINUED	$ 34.00	$ 275.00
BCH87-2	HOME TOWN CHURCH (1987 - 1988)	671-8	Porcelain	NO	✓	DISCONTINUED	40.00	300.00
BCH88-1	HOME TOWN DRUGSTORE (1988 - 1989)	672-6	Porcelain	NO	✓	DISCONTINUED	40.00	675.00
	Same mold as the Christmas In The City Variety Store.							

CLIPBOARD
• Pieces were available in stores as a "Purchase With Purchase."
• Fourth piece, a Bookstore, was created to fit snugly against the Drugstore but was never produced.
• Boardinghouse and Church have edition limits under 5,000 pieces each, Drugstore under 3,000 pieces.

The Heritage Village Collection ™

DV84-1

THE ORIGINAL SHOPS OF DICKENS' VILLAGE:

CROWNTREE INN

CANDLE SHOP

GREEN GROCER

GOLDEN SWAN BAKER

BEAN AND SON SMITHY SHOP

ABEL BEESLEY BUTCHER

JONES & CO. BRUSH & BASKET SHOP

DV84-2

CROWNTREE INN

Large multi-paned windows run length of front of Inn with entry door decorated by wreath, second story stone, attic dormer.

DV84-3

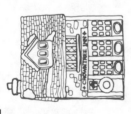

CANDLE SHOP

Timber framed windows, plaster over stone small house/store. Rental rooms in attic, light over open front door.

DV84-4

GREEN GROCER

Thatched roof over timbered two story grocery/provisions store. Bay window for display. Attached storage room on side of store.

DV84-5

GOLDEN SWAN BAKER

Painted sign with gold swan hangs above large bay window for display. Timbered building, brick chimney, light above entry door.

DV84-6

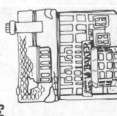

BEAN AND SON SMITHY SHOP

Double wood door, stone first story, second story set upon stone with overhang. Steep curved roof with one brick chimney.

DV84-7

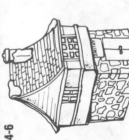

ABEL BEESLEY BUTCHER

Timbered bottom half, second story plaster over stone, two chimneys.

DV84-8

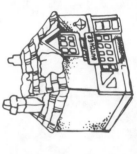

JONES & CO. BRUSH & BASKET SHOP

Cellar shop is a cobbler with small sign by his door to advertise, rest of building is for basketry, mats, and brush. Narrow staircase leads to entry. House rises 2 1/2 stories plus cellar at ground level.

ART CHART #	NAME	ITEM #	MATERIAL	SET?	⟳■	MARKET STATUS	ORIGINAL SRP	GREENBOOK MKT PRICE
	VARIATIONS/MISC/COLLECTOR NOTES							
DV84-1	THE ORIGINAL SHOPS OF DICKENS' VILLAGE	6515-3	Porcelain	SET OF 7	✓	RETIRED 1988	$175.00	$1375.00
DV84-2	CROWNTREE INN	6515-3	Porcelain	1 of a 7 pc set	✓	RETIRED 1988	25.00	350.00
DV84-3	CANDLE SHOP	6515-3	Porcelain	1 of a 7 pc set	✓	RETIRED 1988	25.00	210.00
	Variations in roof color.							
DV84-4	GREEN GROCER	6515-3	Porcelain	1 of a 7 pc set	✓	RETIRED 1988	25.00	200.00
DV84-5	GOLDEN SWAN BAKER	6515-3	Porcelain	1 of a 7 pc set	✓	RETIRED 1988	25.00	155.00
DV84-6	BEAN AND SON SMITHY SHOP	6515-3	Porcelain	1 of a 7 pc set	✓	RETIRED 1988	25.00	185.00
DV84-7	ABEL BEESLEY BUTCHER	6515-3	Porcelain	1 of a 7 pc set	✓	RETIRED 1988	25.00	145.00
DV84-8	JONES & CO. BRUSH & BASKET SHOP	6515-3	Porcelain	1 of a 7 pc set	✓	RETIRED 1988	25.00	355.00

THE HERITAGE VILLAGE COLLECTION – DICKENS VILLAGE

1985   1985

DV85-1

DICKENS' VILLAGE CHURCH
Stone church with entry at base of massive turret. Nave has exposed stone base with timber/plaster upper walls. Irregular shingled roof. Turret bell chamber has rounded arches. Entry door and nave windows demonstrate a more pointed arch shape.

DV85-2

DICKENS' COTTAGES:

THATCHED COTTAGE
STONE COTTAGE
TUDOR COTTAGE

DV85-3

THATCHED COTTAGE
Double chimneys rise from thatched roof, second story plastered/timbered home with second story extending out on sides.

DV85-4

STONE COTTAGE
Varigated fieldstone walls crowned with rough-hewn shingle roof. House has two wings each with own chimney.

DV85-5

TUDOR COTTAGE
Stone foundation with timbered/plastered walls forming a small house. Two chimneys for heating/cooking.

DV85-6

DICKENS' VILLAGE MILL
Rough-hewn stone makes up 3 section mill with large wooden millwheel. Two sets double doors – one large set to allow carriage to be brought directly into building, smaller doors open into silo area. Pronounced roof ridges on two sections.

ART CHART #	NAME	ITEM #	MATERIAL	SET?	⬥	MARKET STATUS	ORIGINAL SRP	GREENBOOK MKT PRICE
	VARIATIONS/MISC/COLLECTOR NOTES							
DV85-1	DICKENS' VILLAGE CHURCH	6516-1	Porcelain	NO	✓	RETIRED 1989	$ 35.00	See Below
	Variations in color affect Market Price: "Green" @ $350, "Cream" @ $285, "Dark" @ $155, and "Tan" @ $170. See page 225.							
DV85-2	DICKENS' COTTAGES	6518-8	Porcelain	SET OF 3	✓	RETIRED 1988	75.00	$ 1015.00
	Early release to Gift Creations Concepts.							
DV85-3	THATCHED COTTAGE	6518-8	Porcelain	1 of a 3 pc set	✓	RETIRED 1988	25.00	210.00
	Early release to Gift Creations Concepts.							
DV85-4	STONE COTTAGE	6518-8	Porcelain	1 of a 3 pc set	✓	RETIRED 1988	25.00	See Below
	Variations in color affect Market Price: "Early tan" @ $465, "pea green" @ $380.							
DV85-5	TUDOR COTTAGE	6518-8	Porcelain	1 of a 3 pc set	✓	RETIRED 1988	25.00	455.00
	Early release to Gift Creations Concepts.							
DV85-6	DICKENS' VILLAGE MILL	6519-6	Porcelain	NO	✓	LTD. ED. 2,500	35.00	5550.00
	Early release to Gift Creations Concepts.							

DV86-1

CHRISTMAS CAROL COTTAGES:

FEZZIWIG'S WAREHOUSE

SCROOGE & MARLEY
COUNTING HOUSE

THE COTTAGE OF
BOB CRATCHIT & TINY TIM

DV86-2

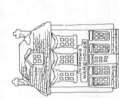

FEZZIWIG'S WAREHOUSE
Squared brick two story building
with two brick chimneys. Second story
front face is plaster over brick.
Entire front is windowed.

DV86-3

SCROOGE & MARLEY
COUNTING HOUSE
Simple rectangular shape.
Bottom brick, second story plastered
with shuttered windows. Bay window
major decorative design.

DV86-4

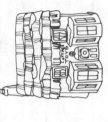

THE COTTAGE OF
BOB CRATCHIT & TINY TIM
Small four room house, main room
has fireplace for heat/cooking.
Half of house rises two stories to provide
sleeping area. Neatly thatched roof.

DV86-5

NORMAN CHURCH
Solid four-sided tower used as both
watch and bell tower. Doors and windows
reflect the Romanesque rounded arches.

DV86-6

DICKENS' LANE SHOPS:

THOMAS KERSEY COFFEE HOUSE

COTTAGE TOY SHOP

TUTTLE'S PUB

DV86-7

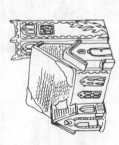

THOMAS KERSEY COFFEE HOUSE
Unique roof set upon simple rectangular
building rises up to central chimney with
four flue pipes. Brick, plaster, and timber
with tile or slate roof. Large multi-paned
windows predominate front walls.

DV86-8

COTTAGE TOY SHOP
Small thatched roof cottage.
Shop has large bay windows
for light and display. Outside side
stair/entry for family to living quarters.

ART CHART #	NAME	ITEM #	MATERIAL	SET?	⟳	MARKET STATUS	ORIGINAL SRP	GREENBOOK MKT PRICE
	VARIATIONS/MISC/COLLECTOR NOTES							
DV86-1	CHRISTMAS CAROL COTTAGES	6500-5	Porcelain	SET OF 3	✓	CURRENT	$ 75.00	$ 90.00
DV86-2	FEZZIWIG'S WAREHOUSE	6500-5	Porcelain	1 of 3 pc set	✓	CURRENT	25.00	30.00
DV86-3	SCROOGE & MARLEY COUNTING HOUSE	6500-5	Porcelain	1 of a 3 pc set	✓	CURRENT	25.00	30.00
DV86-4	THE COTTAGE OF BOB CRATCHIT & TINY TIM	6500-5	Porcelain	1 of a 3 pc set	✓	CURRENT	25.00	30.00
DV86-5	NORMAN CHURCH	6502-1	Porcelain	NO	✓	LTD. ED. 3,500	40.00	3500.00
	Early release to Gift Creations Concepts.							
DV86-6	DICKENS' LANE SHOPS	6507-2	Porcelain	SET OF 3	✓	RETIRED 1989	80.00	490.00
DV86-7	THOMAS KERSEY COFFEE HOUSE	6507-2	Porcelain	1 of a 3 pc set	✓	RETIRED 1989	27.00	150.00
DV86-8	COTTAGE TOY SHOP	6507-2	Porcelain	1 of a 3 pc set	✓	RETIRED 1989	27.00	215.00

THE HERITAGE VILLAGE COLLECTION – DICKENS' VILLAGE

DV86-9

TUTTLE'S PUB

Building rises three stories, ground level has pub for refreshments plus stable area for horse and carriages, second and third story jut out in step fashion. Travelers could rent rooms. Third floor had additional attic rooms. Stone, plaster, and timber, three chimneys.

DV86-10

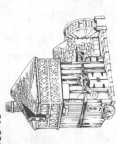

BLYTHE POND MILL HOUSE

Three story timbered house, rough stone wing connects water wheel. Grinding wheels rest alongside house, open front door.

DV86-11

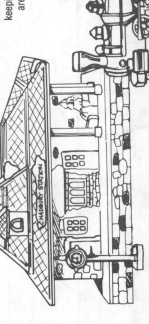

CHADBURY STATION AND TRAIN

Three car train (engine, coal or wood car, and passenger car) and station built of irregularly shaped stone foundation and fieldstone. Columns support overhang keeping passengers dry. Indoor waiting area warmed by fireplace. Wooden benches provide rest area.

ART CHART #	NAME	ITEM #	MATERIAL	SET?	⟳	MARKET STATUS	ORIGINAL SRP	GREENBOOK MKT PRICE
	VARIATIONS/MISC/COLLECTOR NOTES							
DV86-9	TUTTLE'S PUB	6507-2	Porcelain	1 of a 3 pc set	✓	RETIRED 1989	$ 27.00	$ 220.00
DV86-10	BLYTHE POND MILL HOUSE	6508-0	Porcelain	NO	✓	RETIRED 1990	37.00	215.00
	Variation: "By The Pond" error @ $105.00. (Variation is more common than the correct piece.)							
DV86-11	CHADBURY STATION AND TRAIN	6528-5	Porcelain	SET OF 4	✓	RETIRED 1989	65.00	385.00

DV87-1

BARLEY BREE:

FARMHOUSE

BARN

DV87-2

FARMHOUSE

Thatched roof on small farmhouse with centralized chimney. Second story tucked into steeply pitched roof.

DV87-3

BARN

Stone foundation, thatched roof, for livestock.

DV87-4

THE OLD CURIOSITY SHOP

Corner shop for antiques is adjacent to rare book store. Curiosity building has large windows for display. Two chimneys. Book building is taller but narrower. Upper story window and roof dormer supported by wood ribs. In front corner a drain pipe collects from roof and diverts water from doorway.

DV87-5

KENILWORTH CASTLE

Stronghold for Kings and Lords, began as a fortress and converted to Medieval Palace. Stone, thick walled, compact. Battlements surround all turrets.

DV87-6

BRICK ABBEY

Two spires flank front doors, rose window above entry oak doors. Example of a stage of Gothic architecture.

DV87-7

CHESTERTON MANOR HOUSE

Known as a Great House, set into countryside on acres of estate land. Stone facade, slate roof, area of plaster and half timber, open pediment above wood entry doors. Double roof peaks above central hall.

ART CHART #	NAME	ITEM #	MATERIAL	SET?	🔄	MARKET STATUS	ORIGINAL SRP	GREENBOOK MKT PRICE
				VARIATIONS/MISC/COLLECTOR NOTES				
DV87-1	**BARLEY BREE**	**5900-5**	**Porcelain**	**SET OF 2**	✓	**RETIRED 1989**	**$ 60.00**	**$ 370.00**
DV87-2	FARMHOUSE	5900-5	Porcelain	1 of 2 pc set	✓	RETIRED 1989	30.00	NE
DV87-3	BARN	5900-5	Porcelain	1 of a 2 pc set	✓	RETIRED 1989	30.00	NE
DV87-4	THE OLD CURIOSITY SHOP	5905-6	Porcelain	NO	✓	CURRENT	32.00	37.50
DV87-5	KENILWORTH CASTLE	5916-1	Porcelain	NO	✓	RETIRED 1988	70.00	440.00
	Variation: slight size changes over two years.							
DV87-6	BRICK ABBEY	6549-8	Porcelain	NO	✓	RETIRED 1989	33.00	400.00
DV87-7	CHESTERTON MANOR HOUSE	6568-4	Porcelain	NO	✓	LTD. ED. 7,500	45.00	1875.00
	Variations in color. Early release to Gift Creations Concepts.							

NE = NOT ESTABLISHED

DV88-1

COUNTING HOUSE &
SILAS THIMBLETON BARRISTER
Square, tall, 3 story, 3 chimney, offices.
Double size windows, w/shutters, 4 equal
gables create 4 section pitched roof.
Attached plaster/timbered 3 story office is
smaller and narrower. Ground floor
corner wood lattice-work windows.

DV88-2

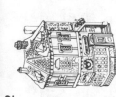

C. FLETCHER PUBLIC HOUSE
5 windows shape corner of unique pub.
2nd story wider/longer, supported by wood
ribs. Sweet Shop tucked in alongside pub
is plaster/timbered design. Both share
roof but have separate chimneys.

DV88-3

COBBLESTONE SHOPS:

THE WOOL SHOP
BOOTER AND COBBLER
T. WELLS FRUIT & SPICE SHOP

DV88-4

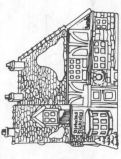

THE WOOL SHOP
Low turret rounds out one front corner
of shop. Wood framing of three front
windows and lattice design.
Light by front door.

DV88-5

BOOTER AND COBBLER
Shoes made and repaired in this stone
building with entry via Tannery where
leather is cured and dyed. Outdoor light
by main display window, wood hatch on
roof opening, mansard roof.

DV88-6

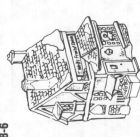

T. WELLS FRUIT & SPICE SHOP
White washed brick and timbered building.
Front window has stone ledge.
Outdoor covered produce bin for food.

DV88-7

NICHOLAS NICKLEBY:

NICHOLAS NICKLEBY COTTAGE

WACKFORD SQUEERS
BOARDING SCHOOL

DV88-8

NICHOLAS NICKLEBY COTTAGE
Brick, stone, and slate roofed home.
Three chimneys, curved timbers
decorate second floor. Bay window on
front room. Two roof dormers.

ART CHART #	NAME	ITEM #	MATERIAL	SET?	↻	MARKET STATUS	ORIGINAL SRP	GREENBOOK MKT PRICE
				VARIATIONS/MISC/COLLECTOR NOTES				
DV88-1	COUNTING HOUSE & SILAS THIMBLETON BARRISTER	5902-1	Porcelain	NO	✓	RETIRED 1990	$ 32.00	$ 95.00
DV88-2	C. FLETCHER PUBLIC HOUSE	5904-8	Porcelain	NO	✓	LTD. ED. 12,500*	35.00	700.00
	*Plus Proof Editions. Market Price for Proofs is not established. Early release to Gift Creations Concepts.							
DV88-3	COBBLESTONE SHOPS	5924-2	Porcelain	SET OF 3	✓	RETIRED 1990	95.00	300.00
DV88-4	THE WOOL SHOP	5924-2	Porcelain	1 of a 3 pc set	✓	RETIRED 1990	32.00	140.00
DV88-5	BOOTER AND COBBLER	5924-2	Porcelain	1 of a 3 pc set	✓	RETIRED 1990	32.00	90.00
DV88-6	T. WELLS FRUIT & SPICE SHOP	5924-2	Porcelain	1 of a 3 pc set	✓	RETIRED 1990	32.00	90.00
DV88-7	NICHOLAS NICKLEBY	5925-0	Porcelain	SET OF 2	✓	RETIRED 1991	72.00	170.00
	Variation: Set with Nic"k"olas Error @ $210.00.							
DV88-8	NICHOLAS NICKLEBY COTTAGE	5925-0	Porcelain	1 of a 2 pc set	✓	RETIRED 1991	36.00	90.00
	Variation: Nic"k"olas Error @ $120.00.							

THE HERITAGE VILLAGE COLLECTION – DICKENS' VILLAGE

DV88-12

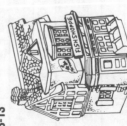

GEO. WEETON WATCHMAKER
All brick, rounded bay window, slate roof, fan light window in oak front door.

DV88-16

IVY GLEN CHURCH
Square-toothed parapet tops stone turret by front entry of a thatched roof church. Curved timber design above door is repeated on bell chamber of turret. Arched windows. This church has a chimney.

DV88-11

POULTERER
Three story stone block and timber, fresh geese hang outside front door.

DV88-15

WALPOLE TAILORS
Stone and brick covered by stucco. Large first floor windows have wood panels under sills. 2nd floor has bow window.

DV88-10

MERCHANT SHOPS:

POULTERER

GEO. WEETON WATCHMAKER

THE MERMAID FISH SHOPPE

WHITE HORSE BAKERY

WALPOLE TAILORS

DV88-14

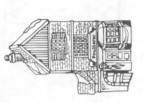

WHITE HORSE BAKERY
Two large windows to display baked goods, roof is hipped and gabled with scalloped shingles.

DV88-9

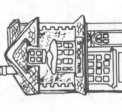

WACKFORD SQUEERS BOARDING SCHOOL
Three chimneys along ridge of steeply pitched roof w/many gables. Classrooms downstairs with student rooms above. Attic windows are shuttered.

DV88-13

THE MERMAID FISH SHOPPE
Roadside fish bins, bay windows, angled doors and walls, wooden trap door in roof.

ART CHART #	NAME	ITEM #	MATERIAL	SET?	🖐	MARKET STATUS	ORIGINAL SRP	GREENBOOK MKT PRICE
	VARIATIONS/MISC/COLLECTOR NOTES							
DV88-9	WACKFORD SQUEERS BOARDING SCHOOL	5925-0	Porcelain	1 of a 2 pc set	✓	RETIRED 1991	$ 36.00	$ 92.00
DV88-10	MERCHANT SHOPS	5926-9	Porcelain	SET OF 5	✓	CURRENT	150.00	175.00
DV88-11	POULTERER	5926-9	Porcelain	1 of a 5 pc set	✓	CURRENT	32.50	35.00
DV88-12	GEO. WEETON WATCHMAKER	5926-9	Porcelain	1 of a 5 pc set	✓	CURRENT	32.50	35.00
DV88-13	THE MERMAID FISH SHOPPE	5926-9	Porcelain	1 of a 5 pc set	✓	CURRENT	32.50	35.00
DV88-14	WHITE HORSE BAKERY	5926-9	Porcelain	1 of a 5 pc set	✓	CURRENT	32.50	35.00
DV88-15	WALPOLE TAILORS	5926-9	Porcelain	1 of a 5 pc set	✓	CURRENT	32.50	35.00
DV88-16	IVY GLEN CHURCH	5927-7	Porcelain	NO	✓	RETIRED 1991	35.00	80.00

DV89-1

DAVID COPPERFIELD:

MR. WICKFIELD SOLICITOR

BETSY TROTWOOD'S COTTAGE

PEGGOTTY'S SEASIDE COTTAGE

DV89-2

MR. WICKFIELD SOLICITOR
Well-to-do legal practice and home. Second story has two balcony areas defined by low balustrades. 3 small dormers. Side door for family entry.

DV89-3

BETSY TROTWOOD'S COTTAGE
Country home – brick, timbered, whitewash. Two chimneys. Known for variations of wall angles. Roof ridge has unique dogtooth design.

DV89-4

PEGGOTTY'S SEASIDE COTTAGE
Up-side-down boat into a house, iron funnel as chimney, captains bridge, crows nest, barrels, boxes, ropes, and boots near entry.

DV89-5

VICTORIA STATION
Brownstone with granite pillars and facings – central section with domed red tile roof, two side wings, covered front drive-through, gold clock above entry.

DV89-6

KNOTTINGHILL CHURCH
Beige/honey stone with grey slate roof, arched windows. Turret bell chamber rises where church wings intersect.

DV89-7

COBLES POLICE STATION
Two story brick, stone outlines front entry and upper windows. Two watch turrets on 2nd story corners.

DV89-8

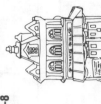

THEATRE ROYAL
Double set of doors and the bulletin board fill the theatre frontage. Garlands and gold bells add festive touch. Second floor rounded arch windows are separated by pilasters.

ART CHART #	NAME	ITEM #	MATERIAL	SET?	🔔	MARKET STATUS	ORIGINAL SRP	GREENBOOK MKT PRICE
	VARIATIONS/MISC/COLLECTOR NOTES							
DV89-1	DAVID COPPERFIELD	5550-6	Porcelain	SET OF 3	✓	CURRENT	$125.00	$125.00
	Variation: with "original tan" Peggotty's @ $220.00. See page 225. Early release to Showcase Dealers, 1990.								
DV89-2	MR. WICKFIELD SOLICITOR	5550-6	Porcelain	1 of a 3 pc set	✓	CURRENT	42.50	42.50
	Early release to Showcase Dealers, 1990.								
DV89-3	BETSY TROTWOOD'S COTTAGE	5550-6	Porcelain	1 of a 3 pc set	✓	CURRENT	42.50	42.50
	Early release to Showcase Dealers, 1990.								
DV89-4	PEGGOTTY'S SEASIDE COTTAGE	5550-6	Porcelain	1 of a 3 pc set	✓	CURRENT	42.50	42.50
	Variation: "original tan" @ $155.00. See page 225. Early release to Showcase Dealers, 1990.								
DV89-5	VICTORIA STATION	5574-3	Porcelain	NO	✓	CURRENT	100.00	105.00
	Early release to Showcase Dealers and National Association Of Limited Edition Dealers, 1990.								
DV89-6	KNOTTINGHILL CHURCH	5582-4	Porcelain	NO	✓	CURRENT	50.00	50.00
DV89-7	COBLES POLICE STATION	5583-2	Porcelain	NO	✓	RETIRED 1991	37.50	85.00
DV89-8	THEATRE ROYAL	5584-0	Porcelain	NO	✓	CURRENT	45.00	48.00

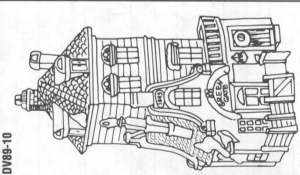

DV89-9

RUTH MARION SCOTCH WOOLENS

Herringbone brick design between timbers decorates front of one and a half story shops and home. Small flower shop tucked onto one side. Bay windows repeat diamond and hexagon panes.

DV89-10

GREEN GATE COTTAGE

Three story home. Repeated vault design on chimney, dormers, and third story windows. Balcony above door. Fenced courtyard and two doors give impression of two homes. Small part has steep roof, crooked chimney, and ornamental molding.

DV89-11

THE FLAT OF EBENEZER SCROOGE

Four stories, broken balustrades and shutters, front door padlocked and chained, ghostly face on door knocker.

105

ART CHART #	NAME	ITEM #	MATERIAL	SET?	●	MARKET STATUS	ORIGINAL SRP	GREENBOOK MKT PRICE
		VARIATIONS/MISC/COLLECTOR NOTES						
DV89-9	RUTH MARION SCOTCH WOOLENS	5585-9	Porcelain	NO	✓	LTD. ED. 17,500*	$ 65.00	$ 405.00
	*Plus Proof Editions. Market Price for Proofs is not established. Early release to Gift Creations Concepts.							
DV89-10	GREEN GATE COTTAGE	5586-7	Porcelain	NO	✓	LTD. ED. 22,500*	65.00	340.00
	*Plus Proof Editions. Market Price for Proofs is not established.							
DV89-11	THE FLAT OF EBENEZER SCROOGE	5587-5	Porcelain	NO	✓	CURRENT	37.50	37.50
	Variation: Cut out window panes @ $115. See page 225. Early release to National Association Of Limited Edition Dealers, 1989.							

DV90-1

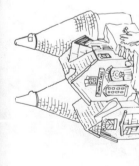

BISHOPS OAST HOUSE

Large attached barn, round cobblestone oasts contain a kiln for drying malt or hops to produce ale. Exterior finished as a rough-cast surface over brick.

DV90-2

KINGS ROAD:

TUTBURY PRINTER

C.H. WATT PHYSICIAN

DV90-3

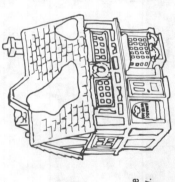

TUTBURY PRINTER

Timbered/plaster design with decorative molding between first and second story.
Ground floor bay window with smaller bays on second floor.
Steeply pitched roof with a dormer.

DV90-4

C.H. WATT PHYSICIAN

Doctor's office on ground floor, outside staircase leads to family residence, bricks used above most windows as decorative arch, exposed stone edges on four corners of house walls.

ART CHART #	NAME	ITEM #	MATERIAL	SET?	♦	MARKET STATUS	ORIGINAL SRP	GREENBOOK MKT PRICE
	VARIATIONS/MISC/COLLECTOR NOTES							
DV90-1	BISHOPS OAST HOUSE	5567-0	Porcelain	NO	✓	CURRENT	$ 45.00	$ 48.00
DV90-2	KINGS ROAD	5568-9	Porcelain	SET OF 2	✓	CURRENT	72.00	75.00
DV90-3	TUTBURY PRINTER	5568-9	Porcelain	1 of a 2 pc set	✓	CURRENT	36.00	37.50
DV90-4	C.H. WATT PHYSICIAN	5568-9	Porcelain	1 of a 2 pc set	✓	CURRENT	36.00	37.50

DV91-1

FAGIN'S HIDE-A-WAY
Two attached buildings in disrepair. Broken shutters, cracks in wall. Barrel warehouse with steep roof, gate across doors.

DV91-2

OLIVER TWIST:
BROWNLOW HOUSE
MAYLIE COTTAGE

DV91-3

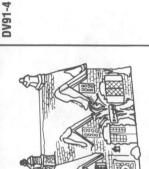

BROWNLOW HOUSE
Two story stone house with two brick chimneys and three front gables. Double doors.

DV91-4

MAYLIE COTTAGE
Pronounced roof ridge. Curved cone roof shape repeated on dormers and front door. One chimney rises up front facade, second chimney on side of house.

DV91-5

ASHBURY INN
Tudor timbered Inn for coach travelers. Food, lodging, and drink. Double chimneys, two roof dormers, and double peaks over multi-paned windows by entry.

DV91-6

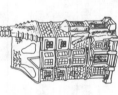

NEPHEW FRED'S FLAT
Four story home with bow windows rising from second floor to roof like a turret. Planters flank front door. Side door with projecting window overhead and crowstepped coping in gable rising to two chimneys. Ivy grows up corner area - garlands, wreaths, and Christmas greetings decorate facade.

ART CHART #	NAME	ITEM #	MATERIAL	SET?	🖐	MARKET STATUS	ORIGINAL SRP	GREENBOOK MKT PRICE
			VARIATIONS/MISC/COLLECTOR NOTES					
DV91-1	FAGIN'S HIDE-A-WAY	5552-2	Porcelain	NO	✓	CURRENT	$ 68.00	$ 68.00
DV91-2	OLIVER TWIST	5553-0	Porcelain	SET OF 2	✓	CURRENT	75.00	75.00
DV91-3	BROWNLOW HOUSE	5553-0	Porcelain	1 of a 2 pc set	✓	CURRENT	37.50	37.50
DV91-4	MAYLIE COTTAGE	5553-0	Porcelain	1 of a 2 pc set	✓	CURRENT	37.50	37.50
DV91-5	ASHBURY INN	5555-7	Porcelain	NO	✓	CURRENT	55.00	55.00
DV91-6	NEPHEW FRED'S FLAT	5557-3	Porcelain	NO	✓	CURRENT	35.00	35.00

DV92-1

DV92-2

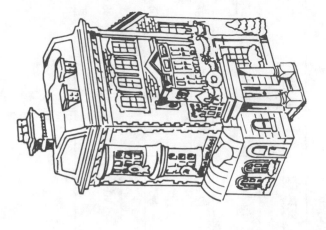

CROWN & CRICKET INN

Three story brick and stone Inn. Pillars flank covered entry.
Curved hood extends over Golden Lion Arms Pub on side. Wrought iron balustrade
outlines front triple window on second floor. Dressed stone edges walls.
Mansard roof with decorative edge trim and molding.

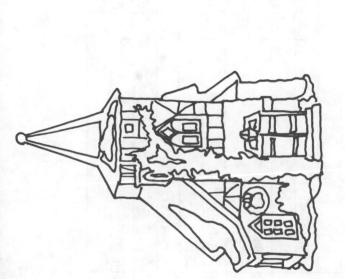

OLD MICHAELCHURCH

Stone base with lath and plaster filling space between timbered upper portion.
Tower rises up front facade with heavy solid look, a simple four sided structure.
Double wood doors at tower base. Chimney at rear of church.

ART CHART #	NAME	ITEM #	MATERIAL	SET?	☺▪	MARKET STATUS	ORIGINAL SRP	GREENBOOK MKT PRICE
			VARIATIONS/MISC/COLLECTOR NOTES					
DV92-1	OLD MICHAELCHURCH	5562-0	Porcelain	NO	✓	CURRENT	$ 42.00	$ 42.00
	Early release to Showcase Dealers and Gift Creations Concepts.							
DV92-2	CROWN & CRICKET INN	5750-9	Porcelain	NO	✓	1992 ANNUAL	100.00	100.00
	1st Edition Charles Dickens' Signature Series©. (An announced Series of 4.) Special collector box and hang tag.							

NE86-1

NEW ENGLAND VILLAGE:

APOTHECARY SHOP

GENERAL STORE

NATHANIEL BINGHAM FABRICS

LIVERY STABLE & BOOT SHOP

STEEPLE CHURCH

BRICK TOWN HALL

RED SCHOOLHOUSE

NE86-2

APOTHECARY SHOP
Varigated fieldstone with white wood bay window. Gable and lean-to are blue clapboard.

NE86-3

GENERAL STORE
Round columns support full length covered porch. Large multi-paned window allows one to see the goods for sale. Two small dormers on roof with central chimney.

NE86-4

NATHANIEL BINGHAM FABRICS
Clapboard saltbox design fabric store and Post Office. Each shop has own chimney. Living quarters above larger fabric store.

NE86-5

LIVERY STABLE & BOOT SHOP
Two story painted clapboard house with wood planked wing contains tannery and livery stable. Stable has stone chimney, double doors.

NE86-6

STEEPLE CHURCH
White clapboard church w/tier 2 steeple. Windows have molding above and below. Simple design characteristic of area.

NE86-7

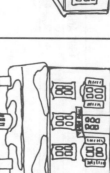

BRICK TOWN HALL
Mansard roof over two story Town Hall. Cupola is centered on roof ridge between two brick chimneys. Windows trimmed with ornamental molding.

NE86-8

RED SCHOOLHOUSE
Red wood school with stone chimney and open belfry. Hand powered water pump by front door.

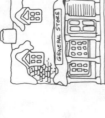

ART CHART #	NAME	ITEM #	MATERIAL	SET?	🖐	MARKET STATUS	ORIGINAL SRP	GREENBOOK MKT PRICE
	VARIATIONS/MISC/COLLECTOR NOTES							
NE86-1	NEW ENGLAND VILLAGE	6530-7	Porcelain	SET OF 7	✓	RETIRED 1989	$170.00	$950.00
NE86-2	APOTHECARY SHOP	6530-7	Porcelain	1 of a 7 pc set	✓	RETIRED 1989	25.00	80.00
NE86-3	GENERAL STORE	6530-7	Porcelain	1 of a 7 pc set	✓	RETIRED 1989	25.00	250.00
NE86-4	NATHANIEL BINGHAM FABRICS	6530-7	Porcelain	1 of a 7 pc set	✓	RETIRED 1989	25.00	125.00
NE86-5	LIVERY STABLE & BOOT SHOP	6530-7	Porcelain	1 of a 7 pc set	✓	RETIRED 1989	25.00	105.00
NE86-6	STEEPLE CHURCH	6530-7	Porcelain	1 of a 7 pc set	✓	RETIRED 1989	25.00	130.00
	Re-issued in 1989 as #6539-0 (NE89-4) when #6530-7 retired along with 6 other pieces of the New England Village set. The trees are part of the mold on original #6530-7, trees are glued on in #6539-0. See page 225.							
NE86-7	BRICK TOWN HALL	6530-7	Porcelain	1 of a 7 pc set	✓	RETIRED 1989	25.00	190.00
NE86-8	RED SCHOOLHOUSE	6530-7	Porcelain	1 of a 7 pc set	✓	RETIRED 1989	25.00	210.00

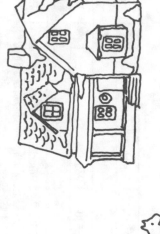

JACOB ADAMS FARMHOUSE AND BARN

Red multi-level wood barn atop a stone foundation.

Home features front porch, small front bay window, butter churn by door, simple design.

Stone silo attached.

ART CHART #	NAME	ITEM #	MATERIAL	SET?	⟳	MARKET STATUS	ORIGINAL SRP	GREENBOOK MKT PRICE
NE86-9	JACOB ADAMS FARMHOUSE AND BARN	6538-2	Porcelain	SET OF 5	✓	RETIRED 1989	$ 65.00	$ 375.00

VARIATIONS/MISC/COLLECTOR NOTES

NE87-1

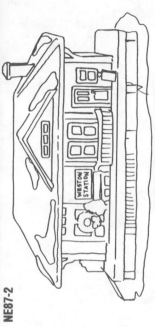

CRAGGY COVE LIGHTHOUSE

Keeper lives in small white clapboard home attached to lighthouse.
Front porch of home features holiday decorated columns.
Stone house foundation, whitewashed brick light tower.

NE87-2

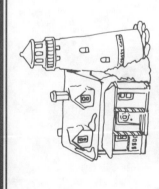

WESTON TRAIN STATION

Luggage ramps lead to platform where you puchase tickets
and wait inside or on benches outside.   Wheeled luggage cart stands on
side of building.   White with blue trim and red roof.

NE87-3

SMYTHE WOOLEN MILL

Fabric woven for manufacture into clothing, yard goods.
Hydro powered by water wheel.   Stone base with wood upper stories.
Bales of wool stacked outside office door.   Lower windows each with shutter.

NE87-4

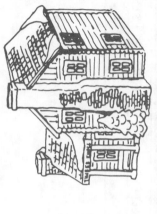

TIMBER KNOLL LOG CABIN

Two stone chimneys and fireplace provide heat and cooking facilities
for rustic log cabin, wood shakes comprise roof.   One wing rises two stories.

ART CHART #	NAME	ITEM #	MATERIAL	SET?	⟳	MARKET STATUS	ORIGINAL SRP	GREENBOOK MKT PRICE
			VARIATIONS/MISC/COLLECTOR NOTES					
NE87-1	CRAGGY COVE LIGHTHOUSE	5930-7	Porcelain	NO	✓	CURRENT	$ 35.00	$ 45.00
NE87-2	WESTON TRAIN STATION	5931-5	Porcelain	NO	✓	RETIRED 1989	42.00	215.00
NE87-3	SMYTHE WOOLEN MILL	6543-1	Porcelain	NO	✓	LTD. ED. 7,500	42.00	1235.00
NE87-4	TIMBER KNOLL LOG CABIN	6544-7	Porcelain	NO	✓	RETIRED 1990	28.00	95.00

118

THE HERITAGE VILLAGE COLLECTION – NEW ENGLAND VILLAGE

1988

NE88-4

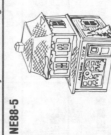

OTIS HAYES BUTCHER SHOP
Dutch door entry, stone side walls, brick front with painted sign over front door on gable. Small size and thick walls plus river/lake ice helped keep meat fresh.

NE88-3

BEN'S BARBERSHOP
A barber pole hangs from front house corner next to a bench for customers. Blue half-window coverings provide some privacy. Water tower on roof supplies the shop's needs. Upstairs office used by a lawyer who has separate entry.

NE88-2

CHERRY LANE SHOPS:

BEN'S BARBERSHOP

OTIS HAYES BUTCHER SHOP

ANNE SHAW TOYS

NE88-6

ADA'S BED AND BOARDING HOUSE
Large family home becomes a bed and breakfast for travelers. Double chimneys. Central cupola and wrap-around front porch.

NE88-1

OLD NORTH CHURCH
Red brick church. First and second floor windows feature sunburst and/or spoke tops. Steeple rises from main entry. Belfry has tiered design.

NE88-5

ANNE SHAW TOYS
Large front windows with window boxes allow a look at toys for sale. Chimney rises from center of roof. Molding beneath roof edge and squared shape give roof a turret look/feel. Rest of windows are shuttered.

ART CHART #	NAME	ITEM #	MATERIAL	SET?	🔔	MARKET STATUS	ORIGINAL SRP	GREENBOOK MKT PRICE
			VARIATIONS/MISC/COLLECTOR NOTES					
NE88-1	OLD NORTH CHURCH	5932-3	Porcelain	NO	✓	CURRENT	$ 40.00	$ 44.00
	Based on Historic Landmark re: American Revolution and Paul Revere.							
NE88-2	CHERRY LANE SHOPS	5939-0	Porcelain	SET OF 3	✓	RETIRED 1990	80.00	215.00
NE88-3	BEN'S BARBERSHOP	5939-0	Porcelain	1 of a 3 pc set	✓	RETIRED 1990	27.00	75.00
NE88-4	OTIS HAYES BUTCHER SHOP	5939-0	Porcelain	1 of a 3 pc set	✓	RETIRED 1990	27.00	65.00
NE88-5	ANNE SHAW TOYS	5939-0	Porcelain	1 of a 3 pc set	✓	RETIRED 1990	27.00	115.00
NE88-6	ADA'S BED AND BOARDING HOUSE	5940-4	Porcelain	NO	✓	RETIRED 1991	36.00	See Below
	Color and mold variations affect Market Price: Original mold, lemon gold color @ $310, original mold, cream color @ $150, and 3rd version, different mold @ $85. See page 225.							

NE89-1

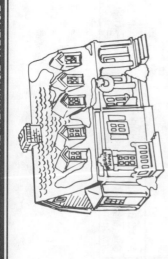

BERKSHIRE HOUSE
Blue dutch colonial inn, two front entries, half porch,
five dormered windows on front, second story mansard roof.

NE89-2

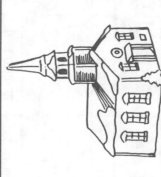

JANNES MULLET AMISH FARM HOUSE
White frame house, fenced yard on side, two chimneys,
gutter and leader to barrel to collect rain water.

NE89-3

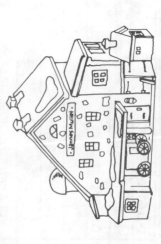

JANNES MULLET AMISH BARN
Wood and fieldstone with attached sheds and silo,
Amish family black buggy stands at barn entrance.

NE89-4

STEEPLE CHURCH
White clapboard church with steeple.
Windows have molding above and below. Simple design characteristic of area.

ART CHART #	NAME	ITEM #	MATERIAL	SET?	☎■	MARKET STATUS	ORIGINAL SRP	GREENBOOK MKT PRICE
	VARIATIONS/MISC/COLLECTOR NOTES							
NE89-1	BERKSHIRE HOUSE	5942-0	Porcelain	NO	✓	RETIRED 1991	$ 40.00	See Below
	Variations in color affect Market Price: "original blue" @ $125, "teal" @ $95. See page 225.							
NE89-2	JANNES MULLET AMISH FARM HOUSE	5943-9	Porcelain	NO	✓	CURRENT	32.00	32.00
NE89-3	JANNES MULLET AMISH BARN	5944-7	Porcelain	NO	✓	CURRENT	48.00	48.00
NE89-4	STEEPLE CHURCH	6539-0	Porcelain	NO	✓	RETIRED 1990	30.00	85.00
	Re-issue of 1986 Steeple Church #6530-7 (NE86-6). See page 225.							

NE90-1

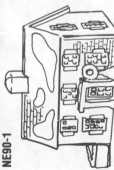

SHINGLE CREEK HOUSE

Saltbox design with chimney rising from mid-roof. Windows have shutters and molding on top and base. Attached shed on one side, with storm cellar doors and fenced side entrance.

NE90-2

CAPTAIN'S COTTAGE

2 1/2 story has balcony full length of 2nd story. Enclosed staircase on house side to second floor. Columns that support balcony create porch for entry. A connected double dormer is centered on front roof between two ridge chimneys.

NE90-3

SLEEPY HOLLOW:

SLEEPY HOLLOW SCHOOL

VAN TASSEL MANOR

ICHABOD CRANE'S COTTAGE

NE90-4

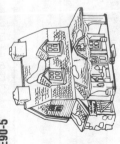

SLEEPY HOLLOW SCHOOL

Framed stone chimney warms log cabin school. Brick and wood belfry houses bell. Wood pile and bench with bucket near front door.

NE90-5

VAN TASSEL MANOR

Yellow house with mansard roof with two front dormers. Wood corner posts support porch. Stone lean-to one side. Double chimneys rise off roof ridge. Four ears of corn decorate front entry.

NE90-6

ICHABOD CRANE'S COTTAGE

Stone first story topped by wood second story. Rough shingled roof with dip in the middle between two brick chimneys.

NE90-7

SLEEPY HOLLOW CHURCH

Wood church with steeple rising off front. Arched windows with prominent sills. Front steps lead to double doors with ornate hinges and molding.

ART CHART #	NAME	ITEM #	MATERIAL	SET?	🐱	MARKET STATUS	ORIGINAL SRP	GREENBOOK MKT PRICE
NE90-1	SHINGLE CREEK HOUSE	5946-3	Porcelain	NO	✓	CURRENT	$ 37.50	$ 40.00
	VARIATIONS/MISC/COLLECTOR NOTES: Early release to Showcase Dealers and the National Association Of Limited Edition Dealers.							
NE90-2	CAPTAIN'S COTTAGE	5947-1	Porcelain	NO	✓	CURRENT	40.00	40.00
NE90-3	SLEEPY HOLLOW	5954-4	Porcelain	SET OF 3	✓	CURRENT	96.00	96.00
NE90-4	SLEEPY HOLLOW SCHOOL	5954-4	Porcelain	1 of a 3 pc set	✓	CURRENT	32.00	32.00
NE90-5	VAN TASSEL MANOR	5954-4	Porcelain	1 of a 3 pc set	✓	CURRENT	32.00	32.00
NE90-6	ICHABOD CRANE'S COTTAGE	5954-4	Porcelain	1 of a 3 pc set	✓	CURRENT	32.00	32.00
NE90-7	SLEEPY HOLLOW CHURCH	5955-2	Porcelain	NO	✓	CURRENT	36.00	36.00

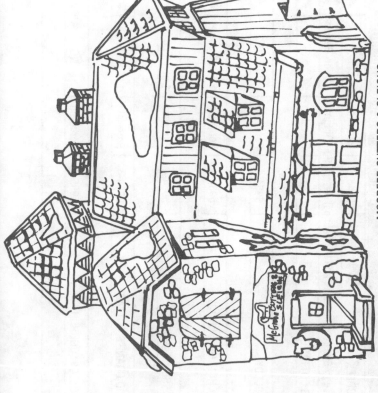

MCGREBE-CUTTERS & SLEIGHS

Builders of carriages, sleighs, and sleds to move people and goods in snowy New England. Stone and wood building.
Large doors in front and side to allow movement of vehicles. Stone half has short tower atop roof. Large loft doors above entry.

ART CHART #	NAME	ITEM #	MATERIAL	SET?	🔔 MARKET STATUS		ORIGINAL SRP	GREENBOOK MKT PRICE
			VARIATIONS/MISC/COLLECTOR NOTES					
NE91-1	MCGREBE-CUTTERS & SLEIGHS	5640-5	Porcelain	NO	✓	CURRENT	$ 45.00	$ 45.00

ALP86-1

ALPINE VILLAGE:

BESSOR BIERKELLER
GASTHOF EISL
APOTHEKE
E. STAUBR BACKER
MILCH-KASE

ALP86-2

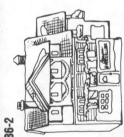

BESSOR BIERKELLER
(BEER CELLAR)

Window boxes on second story hung with colorful banners. Third story rustic timbered enclosed balcony has garland decoration.

ALP86-3

GASTHOF EISL
(GUEST HOUSE)

Rustic inn, fieldstone first floor with two stories of stucco topped by orange/red roof. A third story balcony is decorated with greenery and banners. Window boxes also decorate other rooms.

ALP86-4

APOTHEKE
(APOTHECARY)

Cream walls topped by blue roof. Banners flying from attic window. Prescriptions and drugstore supplies available from store on ground floor. Building shares with tobacconist.

ALP86-5

E. STAUBR BACKER
(BAKERY)

Three story building with bakery on ground level. Third story has some timbering design and an oriel window. Tiled roof and two chimneys.

ALP86-6

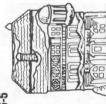

MILCH-KASE
(MILK & CHEESE SHOP)

Milk cans by door denotes shop that sells milk and cheese. Rough slate roof tops blue walls and wood planking exterior. Window box with greenery on second story side wall. Double wood doors allow wagons to bring supplies in/out.

ART CHART #	NAME	ITEM #	MATERIAL	SET?	↻	MARKET STATUS	ORIGINAL SRP	GREENBOOK MKT PRICE
ALP86-1	**ALPINE VILLAGE**	**6540-4**	**Porcelain**	**SET OF 5**	✓	**CURRENT**	**$150.00**	**$185.00**
	VARIATIONS/MISC/COLLECTOR NOTES							
	Early release to National Association Of Limited Edition Dealers, 1987.							
ALP86-2	BESSOR BIERKELLER	6540-4	Porcelain	1 of a 5 pc set	✓	CURRENT	25.00	37.00
ALP86-3	GASTHOF EISL	6540-4	Porcelain	1 of a 5 pc set	✓	CURRENT	25.00	37.00
ALP86-4	APOTHEKE	6540-4	Porcelain	1 of a 5 pc set	✓	CURRENT	25.00	37.00
ALP86-5	E. STAUBR BACKER	6540-4	Porcelain	1 of a 5 pc set	✓	CURRENT	25.00	37.00
ALP86-6	MILCH-KASE	6540-4	Porcelain	1 of a 5 pc set	✓	CURRENT	25.00	37.00

1987

1987

ALP87-1

ALP87-2

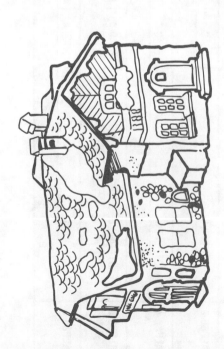

JOSEF ENGEL FARMHOUSE
House and barn are connected. Stucco over stone. Barn has hay loft above animal and equipment area. Shutters swing overhead. Home has balcony above front entry with herringbone planking. Red roof, capped chimneys.

ALPINE CHURCH
Onion dome tops steeple which also features a clock on all sides of the tower.

ART CHART #	NAME	ITEM #	MATERIAL	SET?	✦	MARKET STATUS	ORIGINAL SRP	GREENBOOK MKT PRICE
			VARIATIONS/MISC/COLLECTOR NOTES					
ALP87-1	JOSEF ENGEL FARMHOUSE	5952-8	Porcelain	NO	✓	RETIRED 1989	$ 33.00	$ 450.00
ALP87-2	ALPINE CHURCH	6541-2	Porcelain	NO	✓	RETIRED 1991	32.00	85.00

THE HERITAGE VILLAGE COLLECTION – ALPINE VILLAGE   1988,1990, & 1991

1988,1990, & 1991

1988

ALP88-1

GRIST MILL
Irregular shingle roofing tops the mill that grinds corn and wheat into meal and flour.

1990

ALP90-1

BAHNHOF
(TRAIN STATION)
Stucco upper wall atop tiled lower wall. Ticket window in base of tower rises through roof and repeats tile design. Clock featured.

1991

ALP91-1

ST. NIKOLAUS KIRCHE
Bell tower rises above front entry, topped by onion dome. Set-in rounded arched windows accent nave sides. Pebble-dash finish on surface walls. The home of the Christmas hymn "Silent Night, Holy Night."

ART CHART #	NAME	ITEM #	MATERIAL	SET?		MARKET STATUS	ORIGINAL SRP	GREENBOOK MKT PRICE
			VARIATIONS/MISC/COLLECTOR NOTES					

1988

| ALP88-1 | GRIST MILL | 5953-6 | Porcelain | NO | ✓ | CURRENT | $ 42.00 | $ 45.00 |

1990

| ALP90-1 | BAHNHOF | 5615-4 | Porcelain | NO | ✓ | CURRENT | $ 42.00 | $ 42.00 |

1991

| ALP91-1 | ST. NIKOLAUS KIRCHE | 5617-0 | Porcelain | NO | ✓ | CURRENT | $ 37.50 | $ 37.50 |

CIC87-4

CHRISTMAS IN THE CITY:

TOY SHOP AND PET STORE

BAKERY

TOWER RESTAURANT

CIC87-1

SUTTON PLACE BROWNSTONES
Three multi-storied homes - attached via shared common walls. Three shops occupy semi-below ground level space. Attic dormer windows have iron grillwork as safety feature. Second story attic windows have ornamental pediments and columns.

CIC87-2

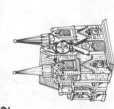

THE CATHEDRAL
Twin spires, early Gothic design, and decorated windows set this Cathedral apart. Stone church incorporates a fortress-like solidness with soaring spires.

CIC87-3

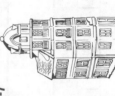

PALACE THEATRE
Mask of Comedy & Tragedy are bas-reliefs on brick building featuring Christmas Show of Nutcracker. Stage entrance on side of building. Flanking double entry doors are display case for Theatre information.

CIC87-5

TOY SHOP AND PET STORE
Width of building occupied by pet shop and toy shop. Ground floor is double high ceilings with half circle windows above store entries. Tucked in at side is small shop, The Town Tailors.

CIC87-6

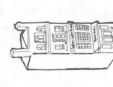

BAKERY
4 story building with Bakery on first two levels. Awning over entry and sign above second floor multi-paned windows. Iron grill work for safety and decor on smaller windows. Two different height chimneys.

CIC87-7

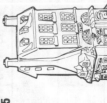

TOWER RESTAURANT
Multi-sided tower structure is integral part of residential building. Double door entry to restaurant/cafe. Iron grillwork for safety and decoration on upper tower windows.

ART CHART #	NAME	ITEM #	MATERIAL	SET?	⟳	MARKET STATUS	ORIGINAL SRP	GREENBOOK MKT PRICE
	VARIATIONS/MISC/COLLECTOR NOTES							
CIC87-1	SUTTON PLACE BROWNSTONES	5961-7	Porcelain	NO	✓	RETIRED 1989	$ 80.00	$ 760.00
CIC87-2	THE CATHEDRAL	5962-5	Porcelain	NO	✓	RETIRED 1990	60.00	285.00
CIC87-3	PALACE THEATRE	5963-3	Porcelain	NO	✓	RETIRED 1989	45.00	1100.00
CIC87-4	CHRISTMAS IN THE CITY	6512-9	Porcelain	SET OF 3	✓	RETIRED 1990	112.00	290.00
CIC87-5	TOY SHOP AND PET STORE	6512-9	Porcelain	1 of a 3 pc set	✓	RETIRED 1990	37.50	115.00
CIC87-6	BAKERY	6512-9	Porcelain	1 of a 3 pc set	✓	RETIRED 1990	37.50	80.00
CIC87-7	TOWER RESTAURANT	6512-9	Porcelain	1 of a 3 pc set	✓	RETIRED 1990	37.50	130.00

CIC88-1

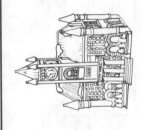

CHOCOLATE SHOPPE

Paneled roof between first and second story extends to shop signs. Building over Chocolate Shoppe rises three stories plus attic. Above Brown Brothers Bookstore is one short story plus attic. Stone facade has heart panels at base while bookstore has sign and canopy over window.

CIC88-2

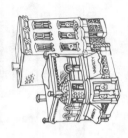

CITY HALL

Imposing fortress with four towers at corners plus repeat design on clock tower. Broad steps plus large columns establish entry doors. Stone arches accent first floor windows plus tower window. Planters with evergreens on either side of steps.

CIC88-3

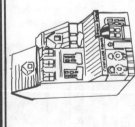

HANK'S MARKET

Grocery store as corner shop with boxes/barrels of produce on display. Rolled awnings over sign. Brick building with painted brick on upper sections of second story. Two upper windows are multi-paned with half-circle sunburst, other window has awning. Two chimneys on steeply pitched roof.

CIC88-4

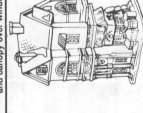

VARIETY STORE

Corner store in two story brick building. Garland decorated awnings extend out to shelter display windows and shoppers. Separate door for upper story. Second floor corner window projects out as rounded tower and support column underneath becomes part of entry. Next door shop is barbershop with striped pole outside. Small eyeglass shop completes trio.

ART CHART #	NAME	ITEM #	MATERIAL	SET?	🏷	MARKET STATUS	ORIGINAL SRP	GREENBOOK MKT PRICE
	VARIATIONS/MISC/COLLECTOR NOTES							
CIC88-1	CHOCOLATE SHOPPE	5968-4	Porcelain	NO	✓	RETIRED 1991	$ 40.00	$ 90.00
CIC88-2	CITY HALL	5969-2	Porcelain	NO	✓	RETIRED 1991	65.00	150.00
	Variation: Smaller in size "Proof" version (none of the boxes had sleeeves) @ $225.00. See page 225.							
CIC88-3	HANK'S MARKET	5970-6	Porcelain	NO	✓	CURRENT	40.00	45.00
CIC88-4	VARIETY STORE	5972-2	Porcelain	NO	✓	RETIRED 1990	45.00	105.00
	Same mold as the Drug Store from the Bachman's Hometown Series.							

THE HERITAGE VILLAGE COLLECTION – CHRISTMAS IN THE CITY

CIC89-1

RITZ HOTEL
Red doors complete columned entryway, red window canopy over each second story French window. Stone, block, and brick building. Cupola on attic window. Slate roof.

CIC89-2

DOROTHY'S DRESS SHOP
Bright green door and awning, bay windows on first and second floor, mansard roof.

CIC89-3

5607 PARK AVENUE TOWNHOUSE
Four stories with ground floor card and gift shop, curved corner turret, blue canopy over double French door entry.

CIC89-4

5609 PARK AVENUE TOWNHOUSE
Four stories with ground floor art gallery, double wood doors lead to apartments, blue canopy over entry.

ART CHART #	NAME	ITEM #	MATERIAL	SET?	🖐	MARKET STATUS	ORIGINAL SRP	GREENBOOK MKT PRICE
			VARIATIONS/MISC/COLLECTOR NOTES					
CIC89-1	RITZ HOTEL	5973-0	Porcelain	NO	✓	CURRENT	$ 55.00	$ 55.00
CIC89-2	DOROTHY'S DRESS SHOP	5974-9	Porcelain	NO	✓	LTD. ED. 12,500	70.00	355.00
CIC89-3	5607 PARK AVENUE TOWNHOUSE	5977-3	Porcelain	NO	✓	CURRENT	48.00	50.00
CIC89-4	5609 PARK AVENUE TOWNHOUSE	5978-1	Porcelain	NO	✓	CURRENT	48.00	50.00

CIC90-1

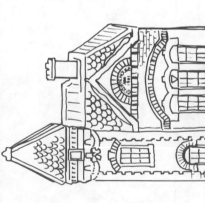

RED BRICK FIRE STATION

Brick Station House for Hook & Ladder Company. Large wood doors lead to equipment with separate door for upper level. Stone block detailing on turret and above upper floor windows. Formal pediment at front gable.

CIC90-2

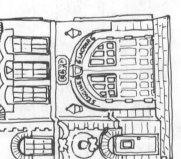

WONG'S IN CHINATOWN

Chinese restaurant and a laundry in brick building. Canopy over entry and at roof feature pagoda shape. Fire escape for second and third story tenants. Chinese characters highlight signs and entry.

ART CHART #	NAME	ITEM #	MATERIAL	SET?	♻	MARKET STATUS	ORIGINAL SRP	GREENBOOK MKT PRICE
	VARIATIONS/MISC/COLLECTOR NOTES							
CIC90-1	RED BRICK FIRE STATION	5536-0	Porcelain	NO	✓	CURRENT	$ 55.00	$ 55.00
CIC90-2	WONG'S IN CHINATOWN	5537-9	Porcelain	NO	✓	CURRENT	55.00	55.00

1991

CIC91-4

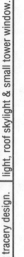

ARTS ACADEMY

Two story brick building has classrooms and practice halls. Corner columns and roof molding frame the front facade. Curved canopy over entrance repeats design of arched triple window with fan light, roof skylight & small tower window.

CIC91-3

ALL SAINTS CORNER CHURCH

Gothic style. Carved support ribs, denote Saints, arched windows, tall steeple with each corner capped by small steeples. Larger windows exhibit tracery design.

CIC91-2

"LITTLE ITALY" RISTORANTE

Three story tall, narrow, stucco finish upper level above brick street level entry. Outdoor cafe serving pizza is behind side swinging doors. Balcony surrounds second and third story.

CIC91-6

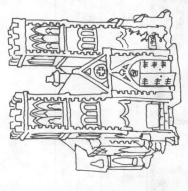

CATHEDRAL CHURCH OF ST. MARK

Front has look of fortification with two towers rising next to entry. Moldings are richly carved above double doors. Stone and brick with accented stone work framing walls and towers. Triple windows on each upper tower side.

1991

CIC91-1

HOLLYDALE'S DEPARTMENT STORE

Corner curved front with awnings on windows, domed cupola, skylights on roof, and carved balustrade design on second story windows highlight store.

CIC91-5

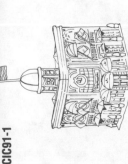

THE DOCTOR'S OFFICE

Four story brick building for Doctor, Dentist, and office space. Bow window is first level Doctor. Dentist windows have broad awning. Third floor window has balustrade design and pediment above, bricked archway entry to side of building.

ART CHART #	NAME	ITEM #	MATERIAL	SET?	⟳	MARKET STATUS	ORIGINAL SRP	GREENBOOK MKT PRICE
	VARIATIONS/MISC/COLLECTOR NOTES							
CIC91-1	HOLLYDALE'S DEPARTMENT STORE	5534-4	Porcelain	NO	✓	CURRENT	$ 75.00	$ 75.00
CIC91-2	"LITTLE ITALY" RISTORANTE	5538-7	Porcelain	NO	✓	CURRENT	50.00	50.00
CIC91-3	ALL SAINTS CORNER CHURCH	5542-5	Porcelain	NO	✓	CURRENT	96.00	96.00
CIC91-4	ARTS ACADEMY	5543-3	Porcelain	NO	✓	CURRENT	45.00	45.00
CIC91-5	THE DOCTOR'S OFFICE	5544-1	Porcelain	NO	✓	CURRENT	60.00	60.00
CIC91-6	CATHEDRAL CHURCH OF ST. MARK	5549-2	Porcelain	NO	✓	LTD. ED. 17,500	120.00	120.00

Early release to Gift Creations Concepts, Fall 1992.

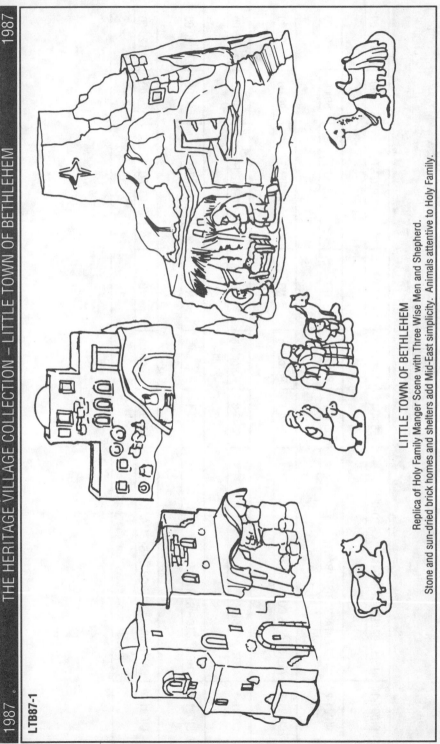

LITTLE TOWN OF BETHLEHEM

Replica of Holy Family Manger Scene with Three Wise Men and Shepherd.
Stone and sun-dried brick homes and shelters add Mid-East simplicity. Animals attentive to Holy Family.

ART CHART #	NAME	ITEM #	MATERIAL	SET?	☺ MARKET STATUS	ORIGINAL SRP	GREENBOOK MKT PRICE
LTB87-1	LITTLE TOWN OF BETHLEHEM	5975-7	Porcelain	SET OF 12	✓ CURRENT	$150.00	$150.00

VARIATIONS/MISC/COLLECTOR NOTES

NP90-1

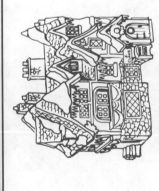

SANTA'S WORKSHOP

Multi-chimnied, many gabled home and workshop. Stone foundation with stucco and timber upper stories. Balconies extend off windows and hold garlands. Mailbox by front door.

NP90-2

NORTH POLE:

REINDEER BARN
ELF BUNKHOUSE

NP90-3

REINDEER BARN

Stone and stucco has stalls for all reindeer. Steeply pitched roof has cupola on ridge and step design on front of dormers. Roof vents and dutch stall doors provide ventilation.

NP90-4

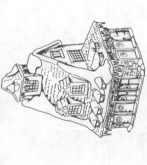

ELF BUNKHOUSE

Home for Santa's helpers, three stories with steeply pitched roof and protected chimney. Made of wood, stone, and stucco featuring bay windows, dormers, and a balcony.

ART CHART #	NAME	ITEM #	MATERIAL	SET?	🔔	MARKET STATUS	ORIGINAL SRP	GREENBOOK MKT PRICE
NP90-1	SANTA'S WORKSHOP	5600-6	Porcelain	NO	✓	CURRENT	$ 72.00	$ 75.00
NP90-2	NORTH POLE	5601-4	Porcelain	SET OF 2	✓	CURRENT	70.00	75.00
NP90-3	REINDEER BARN	5601-4	Porcelain	1 of a 2 pc set	✓	CURRENT	35.00	37.50
	Variation: A name duplicated, another omitted on reindeer stalls. See page 225.							
NP90-4	ELF BUNKHOUSE	5601-4	Porcelain	1 of a 2 pc set	✓	CURRENT	35.00	37.50

VARIATIONS/MISC/COLLECTOR NOTES

THE HERITAGE VILLAGE COLLECTION – NORTH POLE

NP91-1

NP91-2

NP91-3

NP91-4

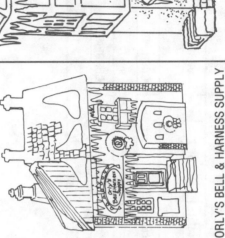

NP91-5

NORTH POLE SHOPS:

ORLY'S BELL & HARNESS SUPPLY

RIMPY'S BAKERY

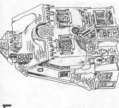

NEENEE'S DOLLS AND TOYS

Rough finish stucco and stone houses dolls, toys, and games.
Steeply pitched rear roof, red shuttered lattice-paned front second story windows, monogram within wreaths.

TASSY'S MITTENS & HASSEL'S WOOLIES

Two shops in connected buildings. Hassel's has corner turret window and oriel turret upper window. Tassy's has angled front window at ground and three arched windows on overhang second story. Gable has carved bough and berry design - roof angles steeply pitched.

ORLY'S BELL & HARNESS SUPPLY

Stone steps lead to bell shop doorway with brick work design to frame it. Sleigh strap with bells above sign. Harness area has large wood doors that open to allow horse drawn carriage or wagon to enter. Window with balcony above, on 2nd story.

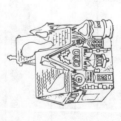

RIMPY'S BAKERY

Three storied, half wood timbered narrow building. Hipped - roof with gable on facade. Large eight paned front window with wood crib in front and on side.

ART CHART #	NAME	ITEM #	MATERIAL	SET?	☝	MARKET STATUS	ORIGINAL SRP	GREENBOOK MKT PRICE
			VARIATIONS/MISC/COLLECTOR NOTES				°	
NP91-1	NEENEE'S DOLLS AND TOYS	5620-0	Porcelain	NO	✓	CURRENT	$ 36.00	$ 37.50
	Early release to Showcase Dealers and Gift Creations Concepts.							
NP91-2	NORTH POLE SHOPS	5621-9	Porcelain	SET OF 2	✓	CURRENT	75.00	75.00
NP91-3	ORLY'S BELL & HARNESS SUPPLY	5621-9	Porcelain	1 of a 2 pc set	✓	CURRENT	37.50	37.50
NP91-4	RIMPY'S BAKERY	5621-9	Porcelain	1 of a 2 pc set	✓	CURRENT	37.50	37.50
NP91-5	TASSY'S MITTENS & HASSEL'S WOOLIES	5622-7	Porcelain	NO	✓	CURRENT	50.00	50.00

NP92-1

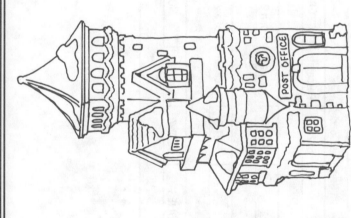

POST OFFICE

Basis for building is turret with what appears to be a half-house on one side of main tower.
Second floor features multi-paned windows, small curved turret between second and third floor could hold staircase and take up little wall space.
Third floor has low balcony outside windows.

149

ART CHART #	NAME	ITEM #	MATERIAL	SET?	↻	MARKET STATUS	ORIGINAL SRP	GREENBOOK MKT PRICE
			VARIATIONS/MISC/COLLECTOR NOTES					
NP92-1	POST OFFICE	5623-5	Porcelain	NO	✓	CURRENT	$ 45.00	$ 45.00
	Early release to Showcase Dealers.							

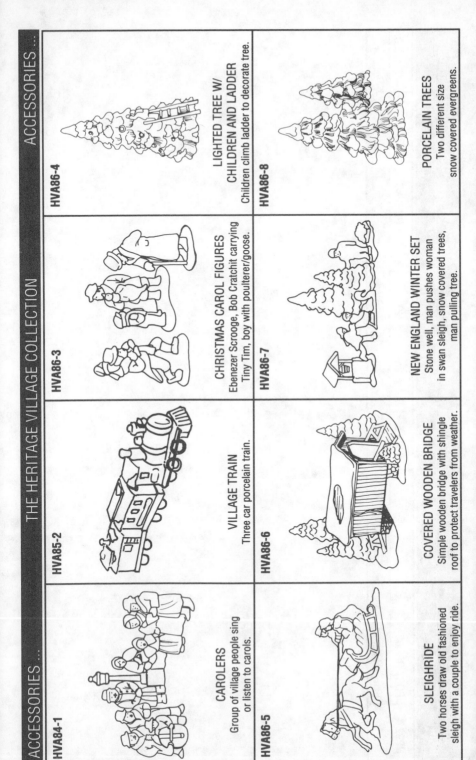

ACCESSORIES ...   THE HERITAGE VILLAGE COLLECTION   ACCESSORIES ...

HVA84-1

CAROLERS
Group of village people sing
or listen to carols.

HVA85-2

VILLAGE TRAIN
Three car porcelain train.

HVA86-3

CHRISTMAS CAROL FIGURES
Ebenezer Scrooge, Bob Cratchit carrying
Tiny Tim, boy with poulterer/goose.

HVA86-4

LIGHTED TREE W/
CHILDREN AND LADDER
Children climb ladder to decorate tree.

HVA86-5

SLEIGHRIDE
Two horses draw old fashioned
sleigh with a couple to enjoy ride.

HVA86-6

COVERED WOODEN BRIDGE
Simple wooden bridge with shingle
roof to protect travelers from weather.

HVA86-7

NEW ENGLAND WINTER SET
Stone well, man pushes woman
in swan sleigh, snow covered trees,
man pulling tree.

HVA86-8

PORCELAIN TREES
Two different size
snow covered evergreens.

ART CHART #	NAME	ITEM #	MATERIAL	SET?	♻	MARKET STATUS	ORIGINAL SRP	GREENBOOK MKT PRICE
	VARIATIONS/MISC/COLLECTOR NOTES							
HVA84-1	CAROLERS (1984) (DV)	6526-9	Porcelain	SET OF 3		RETIRED 1990	$ 10.00	$ 28.00
	There are two versions (sculpting/painting) of this set. GREENBOOK Market Price for the original "white post" is $120.00. See page 225.							
HVA85-2	VILLAGE TRAIN (1985) (DV)	6527-7	Porcelain	SET OF 3		RETIRED 1986	12.00	475.00
	Also known as "Brighton Village Train."							
HVA86-3	CHRISTMAS CAROL FIGURES (1986) (DV)	6501-3	Porcelain	SET OF 3		RETIRED 1990	12.50	28.00
HVA86-4	LIGHTED TREE W/CHILDREN AND LADDER (1986) (CIC)	6510-2	Porcelain	NO	✓	RETIRED 1989	35.00	285.00
HVA86-5	SLEIGHRIDE (1986) (DV, NE)	6511-0	Porcelain	NO		RETIRED 1990	19.50	38.00
HVA86-6	COVERED WOODEN BRIDGE (1986) (NE)	6531-5	Porcelain	NO		RETIRED 1990	10.00	28.00
HVA86-7	NEW ENGLAND WINTER SET (1986) (NE)	6532-3	Porcelain	SET OF 5		RETIRED 1990	18.00	35.00
HVA86-8	PORCELAIN TREES (1986) (HV)	6537-4	Porcelain	SET OF 2		CURRENT	14.00	17.00

THE HERITAGE VILLAGE COLLECTION

HVA86-9

ALPINE VILLAGERS
Seated man, walking woman carrying book, dog pulling wagon with milk cans.

HVA87-10

FARM PEOPLE & ANIMALS
Man hauling logs. Woman and girl feeding geese. Goat pulls wagon and deer eat winter hay.

HVA87-11

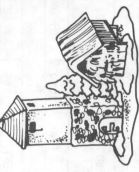

BLACKSMITH
One man tends fire while smithy shoes horse and boy holds pail of nails.

HVA87-12

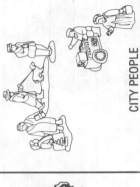

SILO & HAY SHED
Stone and stucco grain storage silo and elevated wood hay building.

HVA87-13

OX SLED
Heavy wood wagon on sled runners pulled by team of oxen. Driver plus small boy holding Christmas tree.

HVA87-14

CHRISTMAS IN THE CITY SIGN
Vertical emphasis on sign for Christmas In The City Collection.

HVA87-15

AUTOMOBILES
City delivery truck, checkered taxi, and roadster.

HVA87-16

CITY PEOPLE
Police officer, man walking dog, pretzel man with pushcart, mother and daughter with shopping bag, and woman collecting for the needy.

ART CHART #	NAME		ITEM #	MATERIAL	SET?	◐	MARKET STATUS	ORIGINAL SRP	GREENBOOK MKT PRICE
	VARIATIONS/MISC/COLLECTOR NOTES								
HVA86-9	ALPINE VILLAGERS (1986)	(ALP)	6542-0	Porcelain	SET OF 3		CURRENT	$ 13.00	$ 15.00
HVA87-10	FARM PEOPLE & ANIMALS (1987)	(DV)	5901-3	Porcelain	SET OF 5		RETIRED 1989	24.00	60.00
HVA87-11	BLACKSMITH (1987)	(DV)	5934-0	Porcelain	SET OF 3		RETIRED 1990	20.00	42.00
HVA87-12	SILO & HAY SHED (1987)	(DV)	5950-1	Porcelain	SET OF 2		RETIRED 1989	18.00	85.00
HVA87-13	OX SLED (1987)	(DV)	5951-0	Porcelain	NO		RETIRED 1989	20.00	85.00
HVA87-14	CHRISTMAS IN THE CITY SIGN (1987)		5960-9	Porcelain	NO		CURRENT	6.00	6.50
HVA87-15	AUTOMOBILES (1987)	(CIC)	5964-1	Porcelain	SET OF 3		CURRENT	15.00	20.00
HVA87-16	CITY PEOPLE (1987)	(CIC)	5965-0	Porcelain	SET OF 5		RETIRED 1990	27.50	50.00

154

THE HERITAGE VILLAGE COLLECTION

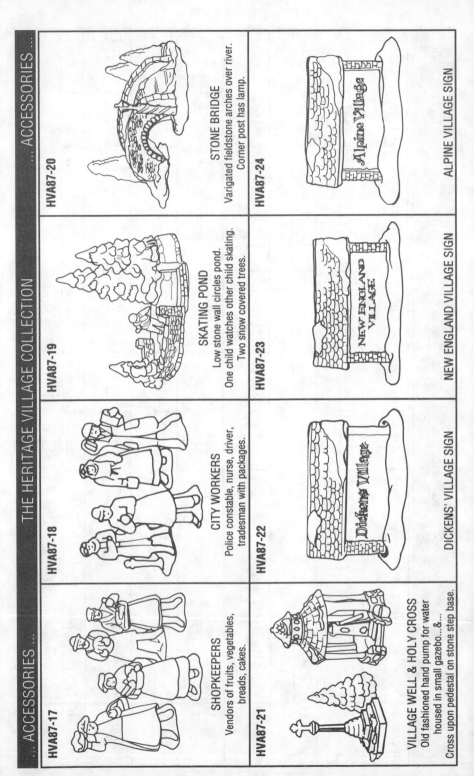

HVA87-17

SHOPKEEPERS
Vendors of fruits, vegetables, breads, cakes.

HVA87-18

CITY WORKERS
Police constable, nurse, driver, tradesman with packages.

HVA87-19

SKATING POND
Low stone wall circles pond.
One child watches other child skating.
Two snow covered trees.

HVA87-20

STONE BRIDGE
Varigated fieldstone arches over river.
Corner post has lamp.

HVA87-21

VILLAGE WELL & HOLY CROSS
Old fashioned hand pump for water
housed in small gazebo...&...
Cross upon pedestal on stone step base.

HVA87-22

DICKENS' VILLAGE SIGN

HVA87-23

NEW ENGLAND VILLAGE SIGN

HVA87-24

ALPINE VILLAGE SIGN

ART CHART #	NAME		ITEM #	MATERIAL	SET?	♥	MARKET STATUS	ORIGINAL SRP	GREENBOOK MKT PRICE
					VARIATIONS/MISC/COLLECTOR NOTES				
HVA87-17	SHOPKEEPERS (1987)	(DV)	5966-8	Porcelain	SET OF 4		RETIRED 1988	$ 15.00	$ 30.00
HVA87-18	CITY WORKERS (1987)	(DV)	5967-6	Porcelain	SET OF 4		RETIRED 1988	15.00	35.00
HVA87-19	SKATING POND (1987)	(CIC)	6545-5	Porcelain	NO		RETIRED 1990	24.00	60.00
HVA87-20	STONE BRIDGE (1987)	(HV)	6546-3	Porcelain	NO		RETIRED 1990	12.00	60.00
HVA87-21	VILLAGE WELL & HOLY CROSS (1987)	(DV)	6547-1	Porcelain	SET OF 2		RETIRED 1989	13.00	98.00
HVA87-22	DICKENS' VILLAGE SIGN (1987)		6569-2	Porcelain	NO		CURRENT	6.00	6.50
HVA87-23	NEW ENGLAND VILLAGE SIGN (1987)		6570-6	Porcelain	NO		CURRENT	6.00	6.50
HVA87-24	ALPINE VILLAGE SIGN (1987)		6571-4	Porcelain	NO		CURRENT	6.00	6.50

156

HVA87-25

MAPLE SUGARING SHED
Two tapped trees, shed with bucket of syrup, & open walled shed w/cooking vat.

HVA87-26

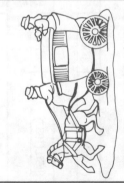

DOVER COACH
Passenger coach with one horse, driver, and coachman.

HVA88-27

CHILDE POND AND SKATERS
Warming house, shutters latch against wind, wooden benches for skaters, brick building with birdhouse above door.

HVA88-28

FEZZIWIG AND FRIENDS
Husband and wife bringing food to elderly neighbors.

HVA88-29

NICHOLAS NICKLEBY CHARACTERS
Nicholas and sister Kate, Wackford Squeers with schoolbook, three children playing, and four-wheeled wagon.

HVA88-30

SNOW CHILDREN
Girl finishes snowman while dog watches. Two boys push off on sled, another bellyflops on his sled.

HVA88-31

VILLAGE HARVEST PEOPLE
Woman with butter churn, man loads pumpkins on cart, corn shocks, and pumpkins.

HVA88-32

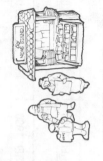

CITY NEWSSTAND
News vendor, magazine and newspaper wooden stand, woman reading paper, newsboy showing headlines.

ART CHART #	NAME		ITEM #	MATERIAL	SET?	🔔	MARKET STATUS	ORIGINAL SRP	GREENBOOK MKT PRICE
	VARIATIONS/MISC/COLLECTOR NOTES								
HVA87-25	MAPLE SUGARING SHED (1987)	(NE)	6589-7	Porcelain	SET OF 3		RETIRED 1989	$ 19.00	$ 130.00
HVA87-26	DOVER COACH (1987)	(DV)	6590-0	Porcelain	NO		RETIRED 1990	18.00	55.00
	Variation: Original "no mustache" @ $85.00. See page 225.								
HVA88-27	CHILDE POND AND SKATERS (1988)	(DV)	5903-0	Porcelain	SET OF 4		RETIRED 1991	30.00	65.00
HVA88-28	FEZZIWIG AND FRIENDS (1988)	(DV)	5928-5	Porcelain	SET OF 3		RETIRED 1990	12.50	30.00
HVA88-29	NICHOLAS NICKELBY CHARACTERS (1988)	(DV)	5929-3	Porcelain	SET OF 4		RETIRED 1991	20.00	45.00
HVA88-30	SNOW CHILDREN (1988)	(HV)	5938-2	Porcelain	SET OF 3		CURRENT	15.00	16.00
HVA88-31	VILLAGE HARVEST PEOPLE (1988)	(NE)	5941-2	Porcelain	SET OF 4		RETIRED 1991	27.50	50.00
HVA88-32	CITY NEWSSTAND (1988)	(CIC)	5971-4	Porcelain	SET OF 4		RETIRED 1991	25.00	48.00

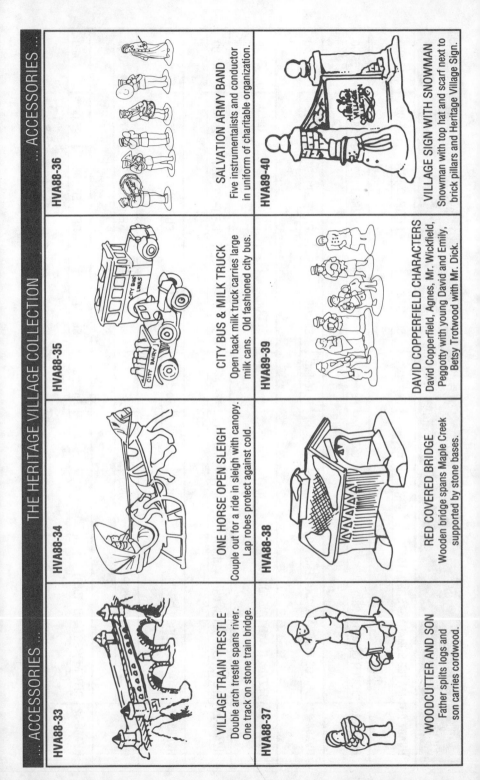

... ACCESSORIES ...   THE HERITAGE VILLAGE COLLECTION   ... ACCESSORIES ...

HVA88-33

VILLAGE TRAIN TRESTLE
Double arch trestle spans river.
One track on stone train bridge.

HVA88-34

ONE HORSE OPEN SLEIGH
Couple out for a ride in sleigh with canopy.
Lap robes protect against cold.

HVA88-35

CITY BUS & MILK TRUCK
Open back milk truck carries large
milk cans. Old fashioned city bus.

HVA88-36

SALVATION ARMY BAND
Five instrumentalists and conductor
in uniform of charitable organization.

HVA88-37

WOODCUTTER AND SON
Father splits logs and
son carries cordwood.

HVA88-38

RED COVERED BRIDGE
Wooden bridge spans Maple Creek
supported by stone bases.

HVA89-39

DAVID COPPERFIELD CHARACTERS
David Copperfield, Agnes, Mr. Wickfield,
Peggotty with young David and Emily,
Betsy Trotwood with Mr. Dick.

HVA89-40

VILLAGE SIGN WITH SNOWMAN
Snowman with top hat and scarf next to
brick pillars and Heritage Village Sign.

ART CHART #	NAME		ITEM #	MATERIAL	SET?	☻	MARKET STATUS	ORIGINAL SRP	GREENBOOK MKT PRICE
			VARIATIONS/MISC/COLLECTOR NOTES						
HVA88-33	VILLAGE TRAIN TRESTLE (1988)	(HV)	5981-1	Porcelain	NO		RETIRED 1990	$ 17.00	$ 42.00
HVA88-34	ONE HORSE OPEN SLEIGH (1988)	(HV)	5982-0	Porcelain	NO		CURRENT	20.00	24.00
HVA88-35	CITY BUS & MILK TRUCK (1988)	(CIC)	5983-8	Porcelain	SET OF 2		RETIRED 1991	15.00	25.00
HVA88-36	SALVATION ARMY BAND (1988)	(CIC)	5985-4	Porcelain	SET OF 6		RETIRED 1991	24.00	40.00
HVA88-37	WOODCUTTER AND SON (1988)	(NE)	5986-2	Porcelain	SET OF 2		RETIRED 1990	10.00	25.00
HVA88-38	RED COVERED BRIDGE (1988)	(NE)	5987-0	Porcelain	NO		CURRENT	15.00	16.00
HVA89-39	DAVID COPPERFIELD CHARACTERS (1989)	(DV)	5551-4	Porcelain	SET OF 5		CURRENT	32.50	32.50
HVA89-40	VILLAGE SIGN WITH SNOWMAN (1989)	(HV)	5572-7	Porcelain	NO		CURRENT	10.00	10.00

HVA89-41

LAMPLIGHTER W/LAMP

Man carries lit torch to light street lamps for evening. Old fashioned lamppost, small tree by post.

HVA89-42

ROYAL COACH

Royal Coat Of Arms on door of gold filigree decorated red coach, wheel base and undercarriage of cast metal, four grey horses with red and gold trim.

HVA89-43

CONSTABLES

One holds club, one with seated dog, one tops hat and stands by lampost.

HVA89-44

VIOLET VENDOR/CAROLERS/ CHESTNUT VENDOR

Elderly woman sells violet bunches from basket, man sells fresh roasted nuts, and two women singing carols.

HVA89-45

KINGS ROAD CAB

Two wheeled horse drawn carriage. Driver sits high and behind cab. Passengers protected from weather.

HVA89-46

CHRISTMAS MORNING FIGURES

Scrooge transformed - smiling, small boy by fence and lamppost - waving, couple carrying presents.

HVA89-47

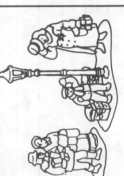

CHRISTMAS SPIRITS FIGURES

Scrooge with Ghost Of ...
1) Christmas Past, 2) Christmas Present, and 3) Future...&.... Marley.

HVA89-48

FARM ANIMALS

Chickens, geese, sheep, ewe and lamb.

ART CHART #	NAME		ITEM #	MATERIAL	SET?	☝	MARKET STATUS	ORIGINAL SRP	GREENBOOK MKT PRICE
	VARIATIONS/MISC/COLLECTOR NOTES								
HVA89-41	LAMPLIGHTER W/LAMP (1989)	(DV)	5577-8	Porcelain	SET OF 2		CURRENT	$ 9.00	$ 10.00
HVA89-42	ROYAL COACH (1989)	(DV)	5578-6	Prcln/Metal	NO		CURRENT	55.00	56.00
	Early release to National Association Of Limited Edition Dealers, 1990.								
HVA89-43	CONSTABLES (1989)	(DV)	5579-4	Porcelain	SET OF 3		RETIRED 1991	17.50	35.00
HVA89-44	VIOLET VENDOR/CAROLERS/CHESTNUT VENDOR (1989)	(DV)	5580-8	Porcelain	SET OF 3		CURRENT	23.00	24.00
HVA89-45	KINGS ROAD CAB (1989)	(DV)	5581-6	Porcelain	NO		CURRENT	30.00	30.00
HVA89-46	CHRISTMAS MORNING FIGURES (1989)	(DV)	5588-3	Porcelain	SET OF 3		CURRENT	18.00	18.00
	Early release to National Association Of Limited Edition Dealers, 1989.								
HVA89-47	CHRISTMAS SPIRITS FIGURES (1989)	(DV)	5589-1	Porcelain	SET OF 4		CURRENT	27.50	27.50
HVA89-48	FARM ANIMALS (1989)	(NE)	5945-5	Porcelain	SET OF 4		RETIRED 1991	15.00	25.00

HVA89-49

ORGAN GRINDER
Man turns handle to produce music for little monkey to dance. Woman and girl watch monkey.

HVA89-50

POPCORN VENDOR
Truck with red and white striped top. Vendor fills red and white bag. Little girl has a full popcorn bag.

HVA89-51

RIVER STREET ICE HOUSE CART
Horse pulls a blue and grey ice wagon for iceman

HVA89-52

CENTRAL PARK CARRIAGE
Grey horse pulls red and black carriage. Driver has mother and child as passengers.

HVA90-53

BUSY SIDEWALKS
Delivery boy, doorman, two elderly ladies, mother with toddler and baby in carriage.

HVA90-54

'TIS THE SEASON
Santa with bell and iron kettle for Season donations. Little girl gives to the needy.

HVA90-55

REST YE MERRY GENTLEMAN
Man sits on bench reading newspaper with purchases all around him.

HVA90-56

TOWN CRIER & CHIMNEY SWEEP
Crier rings bell and reads out announcements. A Sweep in top hat and tails carries chimney brush.

ART CHART #	NAME		ITEM #	MATERIAL	SET?	☻	MARKET STATUS	ORIGINAL SRP	GREENBOOK MKT PRICE
			VARIATIONS/MISC/COLLECTOR NOTES						
HVA89-49	ORGAN GRINDER (1989)	(CIC)	5957-9	Porcelain	SET OF 3		RETIRED 1991	$ 21.00	$ 38.00
HVA89-50	POPCORN VENDOR (1989)	(CIC)	5958-7	Porcelain	SET OF 3		CURRENT	22.00	22.00
HVA89-51	RIVER STREET ICE HOUSE CART (1989)	(CIC)	5959-5	Porcelain	NO		RETIRED 1991	20.00	40.00
HVA89-52	CENTRAL PARK CARRIAGE (1989)	(CIC)	5979-0	Porcelain	NO		CURRENT	30.00	30.00
HVA90-53	BUSY SIDEWALKS (1990)	(CIC)	5535-2	Porcelain	SET OF 4		CURRENT	28.00	28.00
HVA90-54	'TIS THE SEASON (1990)	(CIC)	5539-5	Porcelain	NO		CURRENT	12.50	12.50
HVA90-55	REST YE MERRY GENTLEMAN (1990)	(CIC)	5540-9	Prcln/Metal	NO		CURRENT	12.50	12.50
HVA90-56	TOWN CRIER & CHIMNEY SWEEP (1990)	(DV)	5569-7	Porcelain	SET OF 2		CURRENT	15.00	15.00

THE HERITAGE VILLAGE COLLECTION

HVA90-57

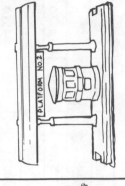

CAROLERS ON THE DOORSTEP
Four children sing carols to elderly man and woman - boys carry lanterns, girls have songbooks.

HVA90-58

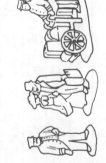

HOLIDAY TRAVELERS
Train conductor, baggage handler, and man and woman passengers.

HVA90-59

THE FLYING SCOT TRAIN
Engine and wood supply car and two passenger cars with luggage carriers atop cars.

HVA90-60

VICTORIA STATION TRAIN PLATFORM
Ticket booth with windows all around, long metal roof to protect passengers.

HVA90-61

TRIMMING THE NORTH POLE
One elf holds another to put greenery on North Pole sign while blue bird watches.

HVA90-62

SANTA & MRS. CLAUS
Mrs. Claus with elf waves good-bye. Santa checks book before leaving N. Pole.

HVA90-63

SANTA'S LITTLE HELPERS
Elf stands on presents to hang wreath. Two elves move toy sack. One elf brings two reindeer to sleigh.

HVA90-64

SLEIGH & EIGHT TINY REINDEER
Toys fill sleigh harnessed to Santa's eight reindeer.

165

ART CHART #	NAME	ITEM #	MATERIAL	SET?	MARKET STATUS	ORIGINAL SRP	GREENBOOK MKT PRICE
	VARIATIONS/MISC/COLLECTOR NOTES						
HVA90-57	CAROLERS ON THE DOORSTEP (1990) (DV)	5570-0	Porcelain	SET OF 4	CURRENT	$ 25.00	$ 25.00
HVA90-58	HOLIDAY TRAVELERS (1990) (DV)	5571-9	Porcelain	SET OF 3	CURRENT	22.50	24.00
HVA90-59	THE FLYING SCOT TRAIN (1990) (DV)	5573-5	Porcelain	SET OF 4	CURRENT	48.00	50.00
HVA90-60	VICTORIA STATION TRAIN PLATFORM (1990) (DV)	5575-1	Porcelain	NO	CURRENT	20.00	20.00
HVA90-61	TRIMMING THE NORTH POLE (1990) (NP)	5608-1	Porcelain	NO	CURRENT	10.00	10.00
HVA90-62	SANTA & MRS. CLAUS (1990) (NP)	5609-0	Porcelain	SET OF 2	CURRENT	15.00	15.00
	Variation in title on book: "Good Boys" or "Good Kids."						
HVA90-63	SANTA'S LITTLE HELPERS (1990) (NP)	5610-3	Porcelain	SET OF 3	CURRENT	28.00	28.00
HVA90-64	SLEIGH & EIGHT TINY REINDEER (1990) (NP)	5611-1	Porcelain	SET OF 5	CURRENT	40.00	42.00

166

THE HERITAGE VILLAGE COLLECTION

HVA90-65

THE TOY PEDDLER
Toyman carries tray with toys.
Mother and son look at toy horse.
Little girl holds top.

HVA90-66

AMISH FAMILY
Mother carries apples in apron, father
stacks apple boxes, children sort apples.

HVA90-67

AMISH BUGGY
Amish man feeds brown horse harnessed
to family privacy curtained carriage.

HVA90-68

SLEEPY HOLLOW CHARACTERS
Bram Stoker carving pumpkin,
Squire and Mrs. VanTassel,
Ichabod Crane with children.

HVA91-69

SKATING PARTY
Skating couple, boy, and girl.

HVA91-70

ALL AROUND THE TOWN
Man with "sandwich boards" as a
walking ad for "White Christmas."
Man with packages stops to get his
shoes shined from young boy.

HVA91-71

THE FIRE BRIGADE
Two firemen carry ladder and ax.
Fireman with pail takes moment
to pet mascot dalmatian.

HVA91-72

"CITY FIRE DEPT" FIRE TRUCK
Ladder attached to side, hose and nozzle
assembly on top and rear of red fire truck.

ART CHART #	NAME	ITEM #	MATERIAL	SET?	↕ ■	MARKET STATUS	ORIGINAL SRP	GREENBOOK MKT PRICE
	VARIATIONS/MISC/COLLECTOR NOTES							
HVA90-65	THE TOY PEDDLER (1990) (ALP)	5616-2	Porcelain	SET OF 3		CURRENT	$ 22.00	$ 22.00
HVA90-66	AMISH FAMILY (1990) (NE)	5948-0	Porcelain	SET OF 3		CURRENT	20.00	20.00
	Early release to Showcase Dealers and the National Association Of Limited Edition Dealers. Variation: w/mustache @ $40. See page 225.							
HVA90-67	AMISH BUGGY (1990) (NE)	5949-8	Porcelain	NO		CURRENT	22.00	22.50
HVA90-68	SLEEPY HOLLOW CHARACTERS (1990) (NE)	5956-0	Porcelain	SET OF 3		CURRENT	27.50	27.50
HVA91-69	SKATING PARTY (1991) (NE)	5523-9	Porcelain	SET OF 3		CURRENT	27.50	27.50
HVA91-70	ALL AROUND THE TOWN (1991) (CIC)	5545-0	Porcelain	SET OF 2		CURRENT	18.00	18.00
HVA91-71	THE FIRE BRIGADE (1991) (CIC)	5546-8	Porcelain	SET OF 2		CURRENT	20.00	20.00
HVA91-72	"CITY FIRE DEPT." FIRE TRUCK (1991) (CIC)	5547-6	Porcelain	NO		CURRENT	18.00	18.00

... ACCESSORIES ... THE HERITAGE VILLAGE COLLECTION ... ACCESSORIES ...

HVA91-73

CAROLING THRU THE CITY
Singing man pulls sled with two boys, two women with young girl, man (alone) all with song books.

HVA91-74

OLIVER TWIST CHARACTERS
Mr. Brownlow in long coat, stovepipe hat, walks with cane. Oliver in rags next to food cart as another boy reaches to steal food, third boy holds sack.

HVA91-75

BRINGING HOME THE YULE LOG
Two boys pull on ropes to haul log. One girl holds lantern to light way and another walks alongside.

HVA91-76

POULTRY MARKET
Aproned poulterer holds game bird. Covered stand with display of turkeys and geese. Woman holds purchase as child watches.

HVA91-77

COME INTO THE INN
Innkeeper's wife reads note between sweeping snow from entry. Young boy with lantern lights way for coach driver. Gentleman with luggage waits to board coach.

HVA91-78

HOLIDAY COACH
Four horses pull coach full of travelers who ride inside and on topside seats. Coachman blows horn on arrival as driver guides horses.

HVA91-79

TOYMAKER ELVES
Two elves carry trunk of toys. One elf balances stack of toys. One elf has apron filled with toys.

HVA91-80

BAKER ELVES
One elf holds piece of belled harness from sleigh. One elf holds tray of baked goods. One elf takes a cookie from Sweets Cart.

ART CHART #	NAME		ITEM #	MATERIAL	SET?	♠	MARKET STATUS	ORIGINAL SRP	GREENBOOK MKT PRICE
				VARIATIONS/MISC/COLLECTOR NOTES					
HVA91-73	CAROLING THRU THE CITY (1991)	(CIC)	5548-4	Porcelain	SET OF 3		CURRENT	$ 27.50	$ 27.50
HVA91-74	OLIVER TWIST CHARACTERS (1991)	(DV)	5554-9	Porcelain	SET OF 3		CURRENT	35.00	35.00
HVA91-75	BRINGING HOME THE YULE LOG (1991)	(DV)	5558-1	Porcelain	SET OF 3		CURRENT	27.50	27.50
HVA91-76	POULTRY MARKET (1991)	(DV)	5559-0	Porcelain	SET OF 3		CURRENT	30.00	30.00
HVA91-77	COME INTO THE INN (1991)	(DV)	5560-3	Porcelain	SET OF 3		CURRENT	22.00	22.00
HVA91-78	HOLIDAY COACH (1991)	(DV)	5561-1	Porcelain	NO		CURRENT	68.00	68.00
HVA91-79	TOYMAKER ELVES (1991)	(NP)	5602-2	Porcelain	SET OF 3		CURRENT	27.50	27.50
HVA91-80	BAKER ELVES (1991)	(NP)	5603-0	Porcelain	SET OF 3		CURRENT	27.50	27.50

170

HVA91-81

MARKET DAY

Mother carrying baby and basket and daughter with basket of bread.
Aproned merchant tips hat as he pushes sledge with bagged food.
Man and boy rest on goat pulled cart while standing boy holds bag.

HVA92-82

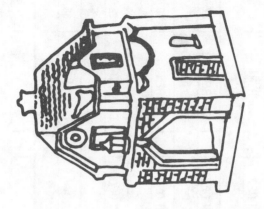

GATE HOUSE

Originated as tower over fortified entrance of a castle's perimeter wall.
Brick base with arched entry made for passage of carriages/wagons.
Windows generally narrow and shuttered to close against weather and for attack.

HVA92-83

CHURCHYARD FENCE & GATE

Stone base with wrought iron atop, acted as barrier to protect land around church
which usually included graveyard. One curved section, one straight section,
one section with iron gate set in stone arch.

ART CHART #	NAME		ITEM #	MATERIAL	SET?	☝	MARKET STATUS	ORIGINAL SRP	GREENBOOK MKT PRICE
	VARIATIONS/MISC/COLLECTOR NOTES								
HVA91-81	MARKET DAY (1991)	(NE)	5641-3	Porcelain	SET OF 3		CURRENT	$ 35.00	$ 35.00
HVA92-82	GATE HOUSE (1992)	(HV)	5530-1	Porcelain	NO		SEE BELOW	22.50	22.50
	Available at 1992 Village Gatherings and select Showcase Dealer Open Houses.								
HVA92-83	CHURCHYARD FENCE & GATE (1992)	(DV)	5563-8	Porcelain	SET OF 3		CURRENT	15.00	15.00
	Early release to Gift Creations Concepts.								

ADDITIONAL VILLAGE ACCESSORIES ...

SNOW

4995-6	BLANKET OF NEW FALLEN SNOW	2' x 5' x 1"	$ 7.50/ea
4996-4	LET IT SNOW CRYSTALS, PLASTIC SNOW	8 oz box	6.50/box
4998-1	REAL PLASTIC SNOW	7 oz bag	3.00/bag
4999-9	REAL PLASTIC SNOW	2 lb box	10.00/box

TREES ...

5111-0	CHRISTMAS WREATHS	Set of 8 1" & .75"	DISCONTINUED
5112-8	SV GARLAND TRIM	3 pcs/pkg Each pc 24" long each	DISCONTINUED
5175-6	FROSTED NORWAY PINES	Set of 3 7", 9", & 11"	12.50/set

	Item #	Description	Detail	Price
	5181-0	BARE BRANCH WINTER OAK, SMALL	Each 4.25"	$ 4.50/ea
	5182-9	BARE BRANCH WINTER OAK, LARGE	Each 7.75"	8.00/ea
	5185-3	TOPIARY GARDEN SISAL	36 pc asst 2.5", 4", 6", 8", & 12"	50.00/asst
	5200-0	FROSTED TOPIARY CONE TREES, LARGE	2/pkg 11.5"	12.00/pkg
	5201-9	FROSTED TOPIARY CONE TREES, MEDIUM	Set of 4 2 @ 7.5" & 2 @ 6"	10.00/set
	5202-7	FROSTED TOPIARY TREES, LARGE	Set of 8 4" ea - 4 cones, 4 oblong	12.00/set
	5203-5	FROSTED TOPIARY TREES, SMALL	Set of 8 4 @ 2" round, 4 @ 3" high	7.50/set
	5205-1	VILLAGE EVERGREEN TREES	Set of 3 3.25", 4.25", & 6.5"	12.50/set
	5419-4	SISAL WREATHS	6/pkg 1" diameter	4.00/pkg

... ADDITIONAL VILLAGE ACCESSORIES ...

... TREES CONTINUED

5527-1	POLE PINE FOREST	Set of 5 4 trees in a snow base, 10" x 5" x 12"	$ 48.00/set
5528-0	POLE PINE TREE, SMALL	Each 8"	10.00/ea
5529-8	POLE PINE TREE, LARGE	Each 10.5"	12.00/ea
6582-0	FROSTED PAPIER-MACHE EVERGREEN TREES	Set of 3 4.5", 6.5", & 8.5"	16.00/set
6595-1	SPRUCE TREE W/WOODEN BASE, SMALL	Each 6"	3.25/ea
6597-8	SPRUCE TREE W/WOODEN BASE, MEDIUM	Each 9"	5.00/ea
6598-6	SPRUCE TREE W/WOODEN BASE, LARGE	Each 12"	7.00/ea

ELECTRICAL

	Item #	Description	Details	Price
	5213-2	"LIGHTS OUT" REMOTE CONTROL Turns lights on/off in up to 60 houses at once	4" x 2.75"	$ 25.00/ea
	5502-6	AC/DC ADAPTER FOR BATTERY OPERATED ACCESSORIES		14.00/ea
	5512-3	HERITAGE VILLAGE UTILITY ACCESSORIES 2 stop signs, 4 parking meters, 2 traffic lights	Set of 8	12.50/set
	9902-8	SINGLE CORD WITH LIGHT BULB	Each	3.50/ea
	9924-4	REPLACEMENT LIGHT BULB	3/pkg 6 watts, 12 volts	2.00/pkg
	9926-0	BATTERY OPERATED LIGHT	Each	DISCONTINUED
	9927-9	6 SOCKET LITE SET WITH BULBS	Each 12'	12.50/ea
	9933-3	MULTI OUTLET PLUG STRIP, 6 OUTLETS	Each 12" x 2" x 1.5"	15.00/ea

... ADDITIONAL VILLAGE ACCESSORIES ...

LAMPS/LIGHTS

Item #	Description	Size/Qty	Price
3636-6	HERITAGE VILLAGE STREETLAMP SET (2 "AA" Batteries)	6/pkg 2.5"	$10.00/pkg
5206-0	SV CANDLES BY THE DOORSTEP (2 "AA" Batteries)	4/pkg 2.25"	6.50/pkg
5215-9	VILLAGE LIGHTS MINI LIGHT SET	14 bulbs	12.50/set
5416-0	SNOW VILLAGE YARD LIGHTS (2 SANTAS, 2 SNOWMEN)	Set of 4 1.75"	12.50/set
5500-0	SV TRAFFIC LIGHT (2 "C" Batteries)	2/pkg 4.25"	11.00/pkg
5501-8	RAILROAD CROSSING SIGN (2 "C" Batteries)	2/pkg 4.25"	12.50/pkg
5503-4	OLD WORLD STREETLAMP (2 "C" Batteries)	4/pkg 4"	DISCONTINUED
5504-2	TURN OF THE CENTURY LAMPPOST (2 "C" Batteries)	4/pkg 4"	16.00/pkg

	5505-0	TURN OF THE CENTURY LAMPPOST (2 "C" Batteries)	6/pkg 4"	DISCONTINUED
	5993-5	STREET LAMP WRAPPED IN GARLAND	2/pkg 4"	DISCONTINUED
	5996-0	DOUBLE STREET LAMPS (2 "C" Batteries)	4/pkg 3.5"	13.00/pkg
FENCES ...				
	5204-3	SNOW FENCE, FLEXIBLE WOOD & WIRE	Each 2" high x 36" long	$7.00/ea
	5207-8	FROSTY TREE-LINED WHITE PICKET FENCE	Each 5.75" x 2.5", 3 posts & 3 attached trees	6.50/ea
	5212-4	HV TREE-LINED COURTYARD FENCE	Each 1.5" high x 4" long	4.00/ea
	5506-9	LAMP POST/FENCE (2 "AA" Batteries)	Set of 10 2 lamps, 4 posts, 4 fence pcs	DISCONTINUED
	5508-5	LAMP POST/FENCE EXTENSION	Set of 12 6 posts & 6 fence pcs	DISCONTINUED

... ADDITIONAL VILLAGE ACCESSORIES ...

... FENCES CONTINUED

	5514-0	WROUGHT IRON VILLAGE GATE WITH FENCE, GREEN	Set of 9 gate, 4 fence pcs, 4 posts	$ 15.00/set
	5515-8	VILLAGE FENCE EXTENSION	Set of 9 4 fence pieces & 5 posts	12.00/set
	5541-7	SUBWAY ENTRANCE	Each	15.00/ea
	5998-6	WROUGHT IRON FENCE (WHITE & BLACK or WHITE & GREEN)	Each 1" high x 4" long	2.50/ea
	5999-4	WROUGHT IRON FENCE (WHITE & BLACK)	4/pkg 1" high x 4" long	10.00/pkg

TRAINS

	5997-8	VILLAGE EXPRESS HO SCALE TRAIN	Set of 5	DISCONTINUED
	5980-3	VILLAGE EXPRESS HO SCALE TRAIN	Set of 5	$ 95.00

MISC ....

	5208-6	MYLAR SKATING POND	2 sheets/pkg 25" x 18" each	$ 6.00/pkg
	5210-8	BRICK ROAD	2 strips/pkg 4.75" x 36" each	10.00/pkg
	5211-6	ACRYLIC ICICLES	4/pkg 18" long each	4.50/pkg
	5511-5	"CHRISTMAS EAVE" TRIM (bulb garland, non-electric)	Each 24" long	3.50/ea
	5513-1	TOWN SQUARE GAZEBO	Each	19.00/ea
	5214-0	HERITAGE VILLAGE MAILBOX & FIRE HYDRANT HV Mail Service - Green & Red	Set of 2	5.00/set
	5417-8	IT'S A GRAND OLD FLAG	2/pkg 2.25"	4.00/pkg
	5516-6	CHRISTMAS IN THE CITY BOULEVARD 4 pieces sidewalk, 4 removable 5" trees, 2 benches, 4 hitching posts	Set of 14	25.00/set

... ADDITIONAL VILLAGE ACCESSORIES

... MISC CONTINUED

	Item #	Description		Price
	5517-4	HERITAGE MAILBOX & FIRE HYDRANT	Set of 2 USPO - Red, White, & Blue	DISCONTINUED
	5524-7	"VILLAGE SOUNDS" TAPE WITH SPEAKERS	23 minute tape, 12' cord	25.00/set
	5525-5	"VILLAGE SOUNDS" TAPE	23 minutes, continuous play	8.00/ea
	5526-3	HERITAGE BANNERS	Set of 4, 2 each of 2	6.00/set
	5984-6	COBBLESTONE ROAD	2 strips/pkg 4.75" x 36" each	10.00/set
	9953-8	HERITAGE VILLAGE COLLECTION PROMOTIONAL SIGN		DISCONTINUED
	9948-1	SNOW VILLAGE PROMOTIONAL SIGN		DISCONTINUED

NOTES

Snowbabies ©

SB86-1

CATCH A FALLING STAR
Seated Snowbaby with outstretched arms.

SB86-2

SNOWBABY SITTING
Snowbaby sitting with open arms.

SB86-3

SNOWBABY CRAWLING

SB86-4

SNOWBABY WINGED
Winged Snowbaby sitting with open arms.

SB86-5

GIVE ME A PUSH!
Snowbaby with open arms seated on sled.

SB86-6

HOLD ON TIGHT!
Snowbaby lying on a sled.

SB86-7

BEST FRIENDS
Snowbabies put arms around each other.

SB86-8

SNOWBABY NITE LITE
Snowbaby sitting with open arms.

ART CHART #	NAME TYPE OF PRODUCT	ITEM #	MATERIAL	SET?	NOTES	MARKET STATUS	ORIGINAL SRP	GREENBOOK MKT PRICE
SB86-1	**CATCH A FALLING STAR** MUSIC BOX (7")	7950-2	Porcelain	NO		RETIRED 1987	$ 27.50	$ 750.00
SB86-2	**SNOWBABY SITTING** LITE-UP, CLIP-ON ORNAMENT (2.75")	7952-9	Porcelain	NO	✓	RETIRED 1990	7.00	32.00
SB86-3	**SNOWBABY CRAWLING** LITE-UP, CLIP-ON ORNAMENT (3.75")	7953-7	Porcelain	NO	✓	CURRENT	7.00	7.50
SB86-4	**SNOWBABY WINGED** LITE-UP, CLIP-ON ORNAMENT (2.75")	7954-5	Porcelain	NO	✓	RETIRED 1990	7.00	35.00
		For smaller version, also in porcelain, see: 1987 #7976-6 (SB87-11).						
SB86-5	**GIVE ME A PUSH!** FIGURINE (3.25")	7955-3	Porcelain	NO		RETIRED 1990	12.00	35.00
		For same subject, miniature, in handpainted pewter, see: 1989 #7601-5 (SB89-2).						
SB86-6	**HOLD ON TIGHT!** FIGURINE (3.25")	7956-1	Porcelain	NO		CURRENT	12.00	13.50
		For same subject, miniature, in handpainted pewter, see: 1989 #7600-7 (SB89-1).						
SB86-7	**BEST FRIENDS** FIGURINE (3.75")	7958-8	Porcelain	NO		RETIRED 1989	12.00	75.00
		For same subject, miniature, in handpainted pewter, see: 1989 #7604-0 (SB89-5).						
SB86-8	**SNOWBABY NITE LITE** NITE LITE (5.75")	7959-6	Porcelain	NO	✓	RETIRED 1989	15.00	285.00

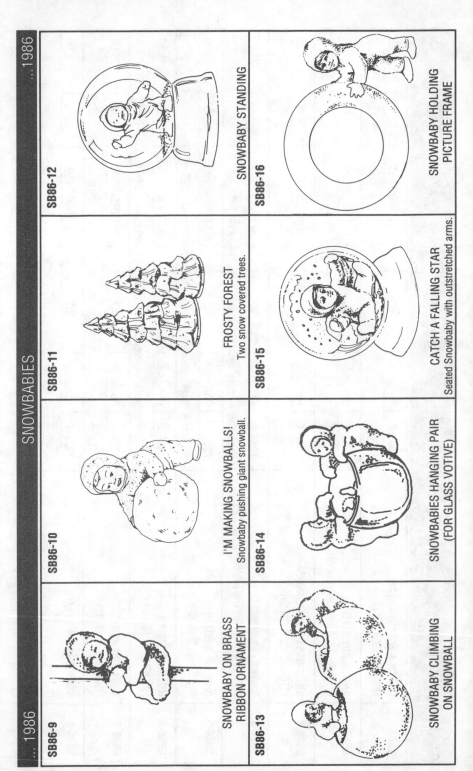

SNOWBABIES

SB86-9

SNOWBABY ON BRASS
RIBBON ORNAMENT

SB86-10

I'M MAKING SNOWBALLS!
Snowbaby pushing giant snowball.

SB86-11

FROSTY FOREST
Two snow covered trees.

SB86-12

SNOWBABY STANDING

SB86-13

SNOWBABY CLIMBING
ON SNOWBALL

SB86-14

SNOWBABIES HANGING PAIR
(FOR GLASS VOTIVE)

SB86-15

CATCH A FALLING STAR
Seated Snowbaby with outstretched arms.

SB86-16

SNOWBABY HOLDING
PICTURE FRAME

ART CHART #	NAME / TYPE OF PRODUCT	ITEM #	MATERIAL	SET?	♦ MARKET STATUS / NOTES	ORIGINAL SRP	GREENBOOK MKT PRICE
SB86-9	SNOWBABY ON BRASS RIBBON ORNAMENT ORNAMENT (7.5")	7961-8	Porcelain	NO	RETIRED 1989	$8.00	$ 65.00
SB86-10	I'M MAKING SNOWBALLS! FIGURINE (3.25")	7962-6	Porcelain	NO	CURRENT	12.00	13.50
		For same subject, miniature, in handpainted pewter, see: 1989 #7602-3 (SB89-3).					
SB86-11	FROSTY FOREST ACCESSORY (5" & 6")	7963-4	Porcelain	SET OF 2	CURRENT	15.00	20.00
		For same subject, miniature, in handpainted pewter, see: 1989 #7612-0 (SB89-13).					
SB86-12	SNOWBABY STANDING WATERGLOBE (4.5")	7964-2	Glass/Resin	NO	RETIRED 1987	7.50	NE
SB86-13	SNOWBABY CLIMBING ON SNOWBALL BISQUE VOTIVE W/CANDLE (3.75")	7965-0	Porcelain	SET OF 2	RETIRED 1989	15.00	65.00
SB86-14	SNOWBABIES HANGING PAIR FOR GLASS VOTIVE W/CANDLE (not included) (3.5")	7966-9	Porcelain	PAIR	RETIRED 1989	15.00	70.00
SB86-15	CATCH A FALLING STAR WATERGLOBE (4.5")	7967-7	Glass/Resin	NO	RETIRED 1987	18.00	NE
SB86-16	SNOWBABY HOLDING PICTURE FRAME PICTURE FRAME (4.75")	7970-7	Porcelain	SET OF 2	RETIRED 1987	15.00	225.00

NE = Not Established

SNOWBABIES

SB87-1

MOON BEAMS
Snowbaby sits on crescent moon.

SB87-2

TUMBLING IN THE SNOW!
Snowbabies tumbling.

SB87-3

DOWN THE HILL WE GO!
Two Snowbabies on a toboggan.

SB87-4

DON'T FALL OFF!
Snowbaby sitting on a snowball.

SB87-5

SNOWBABY ADRIFT
Snowbaby on a snowflake.

SB87-6

SNOWBABIES CLIMBING ON TREE
One Snowbaby watches
another climbing tree.

SB87-7

WHEN YOU WISH UPON A STAR
Snowbaby sitting on snowball.

SB87-8

SNOWBABY WITH WINGS
Snowbaby sits with outstretched arms.

189

ART CHART #	NAME TYPE OF PRODUCT	ITEM #	MATERIAL	SET?	♻	MARKET STATUS	ORIGINAL SRP	GREENBOOK MKT PRICE
					NOTES			
SB87-1	MOON BEAMS HANGING ORNAMENT (3.75")	7951-0	Porcelain	NO		CURRENT	$7.50	$8.50
SB87-2	TUMBLING IN THE SNOW! FIGURINES (2" - 3.25")	7957-0	Porcelain	SET OF 5		CURRENT	35.00	40.00
	For same subject, miniature, in handpainted pewter, see: 1989 #7614-7 (SB89-15).							
SB87-3	DOWN THE HILL WE GO! FIGURINE (2.75")	7960-0	Porcelain	NO		CURRENT	20.00	22.50
	For same subject, miniature, in handpainted pewter, see: 1989 #7606-6 (SB89-7).							
SB87-4	DON'T FALL OFF! FIGURINE (5.5")	7966-5	Porcelain	NO		RETIRED 1990	12.50	45.00
	For same subject, miniature, in handpainted pewter, see: 1989 #7603-1 (SB89-4).							
SB87-5	SNOWBABY ADRIFT LITE-UP, CLIP-ON ORNAMENT	7969-3	Porcelain	NO	✓	RETIRED 1990	8.50	45.00
SB87-6	SNOWBABIES CLIMBING ON TREE FIGURINES (8")	7971-5	Porcelain	SET OF 2		RETIRED 1989	25.00	425.00
SB87-7	WHEN YOU WISH UPON A STAR MUSIC BOX (6.5")	7972-3	Porcelain	NO		CURRENT	30.00	35.00
	Tune: "When You Wish Upon A Star."							
SB87-8	SNOWBABY WITH WINGS LIGHTED WATERGLOBE (5.5")	7973-1	Glass/Resin	NO	✓	RETIRED 1988	20.00	385.00

SNOWBABIES

SB87-11

SNOWBABY-MINI, WINGED PAIR
Seated Snowbaby with open arms.

SB87-10

SNOWBABIES RIDING SLEDS
Snowbabies sled down
hill between evergreen trees.

SB87-9

WINTER SURPRISE!
Two Snowbabies peek out of gift box.

ART CHART #	NAME TYPE OF PRODUCT	ITEM #	MATERIAL	SET?	♪ ■ MARKET STATUS	ORIGINAL SRP	GREENBOOK MKT PRICE
SB87-9	**WINTER SURPRISE!** FIGURINE (3")	**7974-0**	Porcelain	NO	CURRENT	$ 15.00	$ 17.50
			NOTES				
		For same subject, miniature, in handpainted pewter, see: 1989 #7607-4 (SB89-8).					
SB87-10	**SNOWBABIES RIDING SLEDS** JUMBO WATERGLOBE/MUSIC BOX (7.25")	**7975-8**	Glass/Resin	NO	RETIRED 1988	40.00	NE
		Tune: "Winter Wonderland."					
SB87-11	**SNOWBABY-MINI, WINGED PAIR** LITE-UP, CLIP-ON ORNAMENT (2.25")	**7976-6**	Porcelain	2/PKG	✓ CURRENT	9.00	12.00

NE = Not Established

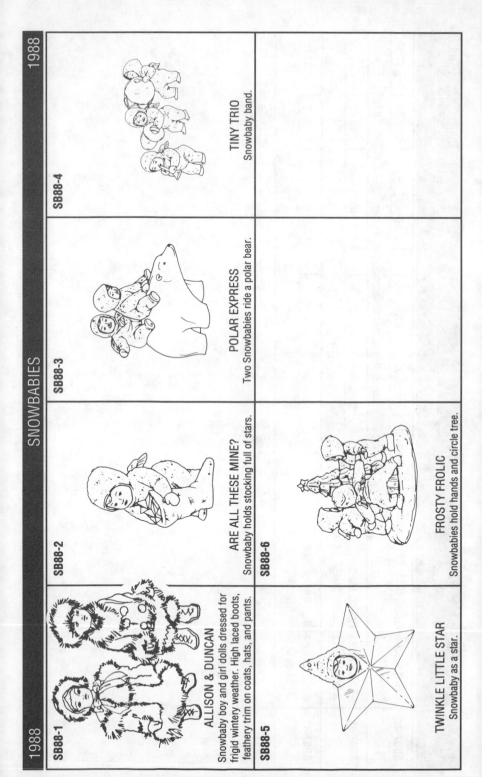

SNOWBABIES

SB88-4

TINY TRIO
Snowbaby band.

SB88-3

POLAR EXPRESS
Two Snowbabies ride a polar bear.

SB88-2

ARE ALL THESE MINE?
Snowbaby holds stocking full of stars.

SB88-6

FROSTY FROLIC
Snowbabies hold hands and circle tree.

SB88-1

ALLISON & DUNCAN
Snowbaby boy and girl dolls dressed for frigid wintery weather. High laced boots, feathery trim on coats, hats, and pants.

SB88-5

TWINKLE LITTLE STAR
Snowbaby as a star.

ART CHART #	NAME / TYPE OF PRODUCT	ITEM #	MATERIAL	SET?	● MARKET STATUS	ORIGINAL SRP	GREENBOOK MKT PRICE
					NOTES		
SB88-1	ALLISON & DUNCAN DOLLS	7730-5	Papier Mache	SET OF 2	RETIRED 1989	$200.00	$750.00
SB88-2	ARE ALL THESE MINE? FIGURINE (3.5")	7977-4	Porcelain	NO	CURRENT	10.00	12.50
	For same subject, miniature, in handpainted pewter, see: 1989 #7605-8 (SB89-6).						
SB88-3	POLAR EXPRESS FIGURINE (5.75")	7978-2	Porcelain	NO	CURRENT	22.00	32.50
	For same subject, miniature, in handpainted pewter, see: 1989 #7609-0 (SB89-10).						
SB88-4	TINY TRIO FIGURINES (3.5")	7979-0	Porcelain	SET OF 3	RETIRED 1990	20.00	75.00
	For same subject, miniature, in handpainted pewter, see: 1989 #7615-5 (SB89-16).						
SB88-5	TWINKLE LITTLE STAR ORNAMENT (5")	7980-4	Porcelain	NO	RETIRED 1990	7.00	30.00
SB88-6	FROSTY FROLIC FIGURINE (5")	7981-2	Porcelain	NO	LTD. ED. 4,800	35.00	715.00
	For same subject, miniature, in handpainted pewter, see: 1989 #7613-9 (SB89-14).						

SNOWBABIES

SB89-1

HOLD ON TIGHT!
Snowbaby lying on a sled.

SB89-2

GIVE ME A PUSH!
Snowbaby with open arms seated on sled.

SB89-3

I'M MAKING SNOWBALLS!
Snowbaby pushing giant snowball.

SB89-4

DON'T FALL OFF!
Snowbaby sitting on a snowball.

SB89-5

BEST FRIENDS
Snowbabies put arms around each other.

SB89-6

ARE ALL THESE MINE?
Snowbaby holds stocking full of stars.

SB89-7

DOWN THE HILL WE GO!
Two Snowbabies on toboggan.

SB89-8

WINTER SURPRISE!
Two Snowbabies peek out of gift box.

ART CHART #	NAME / TYPE OF PRODUCT	ITEM #	MATERIAL	SET?	❓ MARKET STATUS	ORIGINAL SRP	GREENBOOK MKT PRICE
					NOTES		
SB89-1	HOLD ON TIGHT! MINIATURE (1.5")	7600-7	Pewter	NO	CURRENT	$7.00	$7.00
	For same subject, full size, in porcelain, see: 1986 #7956-1 (SB86-6).						
SB89-2	GIVE ME A PUSH! MINIATURE (1.5")	7601-5	Pewter	NO	CURRENT	7.00	7.00
	For same subject, full size, in porcelain, see: 1986 #7955-3 (SB86-5).						
SB89-3	I'M MAKING SNOWBALLS! MINIATURE (1.5")	7602-3	Pewter	NO	CURRENT	7.00	7.00
	For same subject, full size, in porcelain, see: 1986 #7962-6 (SB86-10).						
SB89-4	DON'T FALL OFF! MINIATURE (1.5")	7603-1	Pewter	NO	CURRENT	7.00	7.00
	For same subject, full size, in porcelain, see: 1986 #7968-5 (SB87-4).						
SB89-5	BEST FRIENDS MINIATURE (1.5")	7604-0	Pewter	NO	CURRENT	10.00	10.00
	For same subject, full size, in porcelain, see: 1986 #7958-8 (SB86-7).						
SB89-6	ARE ALL THESE MINE? MINIATURE (1.5")	7605-8	Pewter	NO	CURRENT	7.00	7.00
	For same subject, full size, in porcelain, see: 1988 #7977-4 (SB88-1).						
SB89-7	DOWN THE HILL WE GO! MINIATURE (1")	7606-6	Pewter	SET OF 2	CURRENT	13.50	13.50
	For same subject, full size, in porcelain, see: 1986 #7960-0 (SB87-3).						
SB89-8	WINTER SURPRISE! MINIATURE (1")	7607-4	Pewter	NO	CURRENT	13.50	13.50
	For same subject, full size, in porcelain, see: 1986 #7974-0 (SB87-9).						

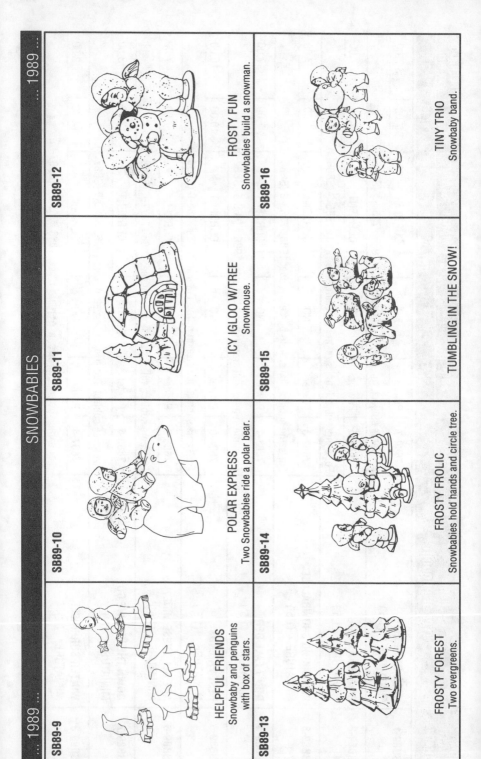

SNOWBABIES

SB89-9

HELPFUL FRIENDS
Snowbaby and penguins
with box of stars.

SB89-10

POLAR EXPRESS
Two Snowbabies ride a polar bear.

SB89-11

ICY IGLOO W/TREE
Snowhouse.

SB89-12

FROSTY FUN
Snowbabies build a snowman.

SB89-13

FROSTY FOREST
Two evergreens.

SB89-14

FROSTY FROLIC
Snowbabies hold hands and circle tree.

SB89-15

TUMBLING IN THE SNOW!

SB89-16

TINY TRIO
Snowbaby band.

ART CHART #	NAME / TYPE OF PRODUCT	ITEM #	MATERIAL	SET?	✆ MARKET STATUS / NOTES	ORIGINAL SRP	GREENBOOK MKT PRICE
SB89-9	HELPFUL FRIENDS / MINIATURES (1" - 1.5")	7608-2	Pewter	SET OF 4	CURRENT	$ 13.50	$ 13.50
		For same subject, full size, in porcelain, see: 1989 #7982-0 (SB89-22).					
SB89-10	POLAR EXPRESS / MINIATURES (2.5")	7609-0	Pewter	2/PKG	CURRENT	13.50	13.50
		For same subject, full size, in porcelain, see: 1988 #7978-2 (SB88-2).					
SB89-11	ICY IGLOO W/TREE / MINIATURE ACCESSORY (2")	7610-4	Pewter	SET OF 2	CURRENT	7.50	7.50
		For same subject, full size, in porcelain, see: 1989 #7987-1 (SB89-27).					
SB89-12	FROSTY FUN / MINIATURES (1.5")	7611-2	Pewter	SET OF 2	CURRENT	13.50	13.50
		For same subject, full size, in porcelain, see: 1989 #7983-9 (SB89-23).					
SB89-13	FROSTY FOREST / MINIATURE ACCESSORY (2" & 1.5")	7612-0	Pewter	SET OF 2	CURRENT	12.00	12.00
		For same subject, full size, in porcelain, see: 1986 #7963-4 (SB86-11).					
SB89-14	FROSTY FROLIC / MINIATURES (1.5" - 2.5")	7613-9	Pewter	SET OF 4	CURRENT	24.00	24.00
		For same subject, full size, in porcelain, see: 1988 #7981-2 (SB88-5).					
SB89-15	TUMBLING IN THE SNOW! / MINIATURES (1" - 1.5")	7614-7	Pewter	SET OF 5	CURRENT	30.00	30.00
		For same subject, full size, in porcelain, see: 1986 #7957-0 (SB87-2).					
SB89-16	TINY TRIO / MINIATURES (1.25" - 1.5")	7615-5	Pewter	SET OF 3	CURRENT	18.00	18.00
		For same subject, full size, in porcelain, see: 1986 #7979-0 (SB88-3).					

SNOWBABIES

SB89-17

PENGUIN PARADE
Penguins follow Snowbaby playing flute.

SB89-18

ALL FALL DOWN
Ice-skating Snowbabies fall down.

SB89-19

FINDING FALLEN STARS
Snowbabies collect fallen stars in basket.

SB89-20

FROSTY FROLIC LAND
Landscape.

SB89-21

COLLECTOR'S SIGN

Snowbabies MINIATURES

SB89-22

HELPFUL FRIENDS
Snowbaby and penguins with box of stars.

SB89-23

FROSTY FUN
Snowbabies building a snowman.

SB89-24

ALL FALL DOWN
Ice-skating Snowbabies fall down.

ART CHART #	NAME / TYPE OF PRODUCT	ITEM #	MATERIAL	SET?	MARKET STATUS	ORIGINAL SRP	GREENBOOK MKT PRICE
SB89-17	PENGUIN PARADE / MINIATURES (.75" - 1.5")	7616-3	Pewter	SET OF 4	CURRENT	$ 12.50	$ 12.50
	NOTES: For same subject, full size, in porcelain, see: 1989 #7986-3 (SB89-26).						
SB89-18	ALL FALL DOWN / MINIATURES (1.5")	7617-1	Pewter	SET OF 4	CURRENT	25.00	25.00
	For same subject, full size, in porcelain, see: 1989 #7984-7 (SB89-24).						
SB89-19	FINDING FALLEN STARS / MINIATURES (1.5")	7618-0	Pewter	SET OF 2	CURRENT	12.50	12.50
	For same subject, full size, in porcelain, see: 1989 #7985-5 (SB89-25).						
SB89-20	FROSTY FROLIC LAND / MINIATURE ACCESSORY (16" X 8")	7619-8	Pewter	SET OF 4	CURRENT	96.00	96.00
SB89-21	COLLECTOR'S SIGN / MINIATURE ACCESSORY (1.5")	7620-1	Pewter	NO	CURRENT	7.00	7.00
SB89-22	HELPFUL FRIENDS / FIGURINE (6")	7982-0	Porcelain	NO	CURRENT	30.00	34.00
	For same subject, miniature, in handpainted pewter, see: 1989 #7608-2 (SB89-9).						
SB89-23	FROSTY FUN / FIGURINE (4")	7983-9	Porcelain	NO	RETIRED 1991	27.50	50.00
	For same subject, miniature, in handpainted pewter, see: 1986 #7611-2 (SB89-12).						
SB89-24	ALL FALL DOWN / FIGURINES (4.25")	7984-7	Porcelain	SET OF 4	RETIRED 1991	36.00	55.00
	For same subject, miniature, in handpainted pewter, see: 1986 #7617-1 (SB89-18).						

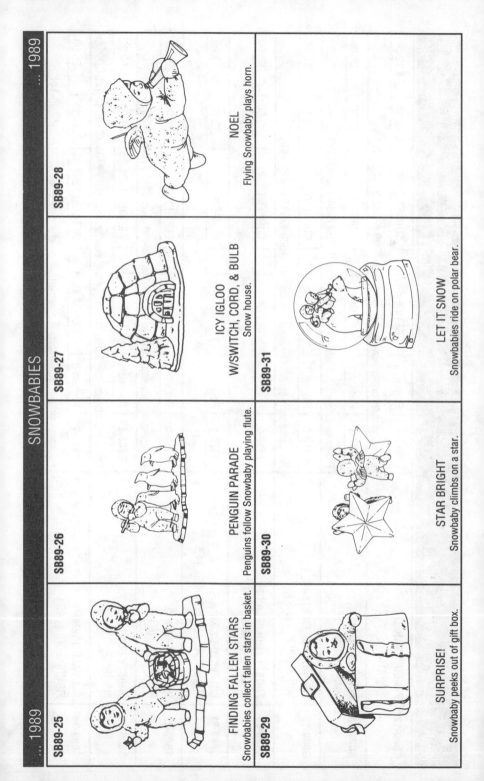

SNOWBABIES

... 1989 ... 1989

SB89-25
FINDING FALLEN STARS
Snowbabies collect fallen stars in basket.

SB89-26
PENGUIN PARADE
Penguins follow Snowbaby playing flute.

SB89-27
ICY IGLOO
W/SWITCH, CORD, & BULB
Snow house.

SB89-28
NOEL
Flying Snowbaby plays horn.

SB89-29
SURPRISE!
Snowbaby peeks out of gift box.

SB89-30
STAR BRIGHT
Snowbaby climbs on a star.

SB89-31
LET IT SNOW
Snowbabies ride on polar bear.

ART CHART #	NAME / TYPE OF PRODUCT	ITEM #	MATERIAL	SET?	☝	MARKET STATUS	ORIGINAL SRP	GREENBOOK MKT PRICE
						NOTES		
SB89-25	**FINDING FALLEN STARS** FIGURINE (6")	**7985-5**	Porcelain	NO		LTD. ED. 6,000	$ 32.50	$ 135.00
		For same subject, miniature, in handpainted pewter, see: 1989 #7618-0 (SB89-19).						
SB89-26	**PENGUIN PARADE** FIGURINE (5")	**7986-3**	Porcelain	NO		CURRENT	25.00	30.00
		For same subject, miniature, in handpainted pewter, see: 1986 #7616-3 (SB89-17).						
SB89-27	**ICY IGLOO W/SWITCH, CORD, & BULB** ACCESSORY (7.5")	**7987-1**	Porcelain	NO	✓	CURRENT	37.50	37.50
		For same subject, miniature, in handpainted pewter, see: 1989 #7610-4 (SB89-11).						
SB89-28	**NOEL** HANGING ORNAMENT (4.5")	**7988-0**	Porcelain	NO		CURRENT	7.50	7.50
SB89-29	**SURPRISE!** HANGING ORNAMENT (3")	**7989-8**	Porcelain	NO		CURRENT	12.00	12.00
SB89-30	**STAR BRIGHT** HANGING ORNAMENT (4")	**7990-1**	Porcelain	NO		CURRENT	7.50	7.50
SB89-31	**LET IT SNOW** WATERGLOBE/MUSIC BOX (4")	**7992-8**	Glass/Resin	NO		CURRENT	25.00	27.50
		Tune: "Winter Wonderland."						

SNOWBABIES

SB90-1

TWINKLE LITTLE STARS
Three Snowbabies sing carols.

SB90-2

READ ME A STORY!
Snowbaby reads story to penguins

SB90-3

PLAYING GAMES IS FUN!
Snowbabies play London Bridge
with penguins.

SB90-4

A SPECIAL DELIVERY
Snowbaby on snowshoes delivers star.

SB90-5

NEVER RELEASED.

WHAT ARE YOU DOING?

SB90-6

ALL TIRED OUT
Snowbaby takes a nap.

SB90-7

ROCK-A-BYE BABY
Snowbaby naps on crescent moon
with garland of stars .

SB90-8

PENGUIN

ART CHART #	NAME / TYPE OF PRODUCT	ITEM #	MATERIAL	SET?	🔔 MARKET STATUS	ORIGINAL SRP	GREENBOOK MKT PRICE
					NOTES		
SB90-1	TWINKLE LITTLE STARS MINIATURES (1.25")	7621-0	Pewter	SET OF 2	CURRENT	$ 15.00	$ 15.00
		For same subject, full size, in porcelain, see: 1990 #7942-1 (SB90-10).					
SB90-2	READ ME A STORY! MINIATURE (1.25")	7622-8	Pewter	NO	CURRENT	11.00	11.00
		For same subject, full size, in porcelain, see: 1990 #7945-6 (SB90-12).					
SB90-3	PLAYING GAMES IS FUN! MINIATURES (1.25")	7623-6	Pewter	SET OF 2	CURRENT	13.50	13.50
		For same subject, full size, in porcelain, see: 1990 #7947-2 (SB90-14).					
SB90-4	A SPECIAL DELIVERY MINIATURE (1.25")	7624-4	Pewter	NO	CURRENT	7.00	7.00
		For same subject, full size, in porcelain, see: 1990 #7948-0 (SB90-15).					
SB90-5	WHAT ARE YOU DOING? WATERGLOBE/MUSIC BOX	7935-9	Never released. Production problems. Penguins on outside of waterglobe too fragile.				
		Tune: "Twinkle, Twinkle, Little Star."					
SB90-6	ALL TIRED OUT WATERGLOBE/MUSIC BOX (7")	7937-5	Glass/Resin	NO	CURRENT	55.00	55.00
		Tune: "Brahms Lullaby."					
SB90-7	ROCK-A-BYE BABY HANGING ORNAMENT (3.5")	7939-1	Porcelain	NO	CURRENT	7.00	7.00
SB90-8	PENGUIN LITE-UP, CLIP-ON ORNAMENT (3")	7940-5	Porcelain	NO	✓ CURRENT	5.00	5.00

204

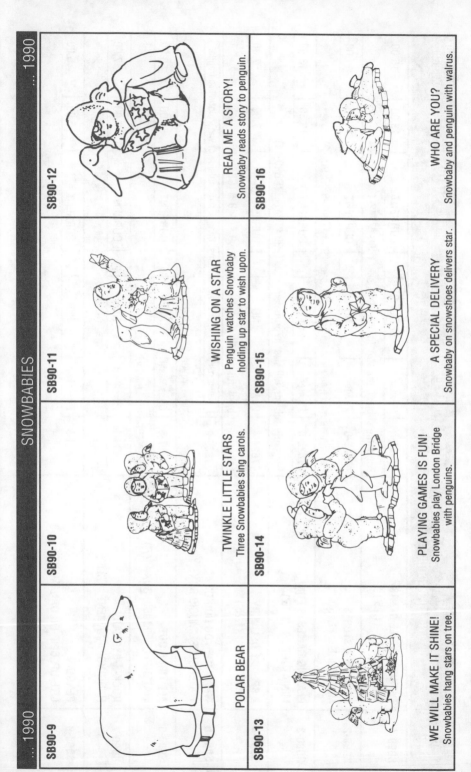

SNOWBABIES

... 1990

... 1990

SB90-9

POLAR BEAR

SB90-10

TWINKLE LITTLE STARS
Three Snowbabies sing carols.

SB90-11

WISHING ON A STAR
Penguin watches Snowbaby
holding up star to wish upon.

SB90-12

READ ME A STORY!
Snowbaby reads story to penguin.

SB90-13

WE WILL MAKE IT SHINE!
Snowbabies hang stars on tree.

SB90-14

PLAYING GAMES IS FUN!
Snowbabies play London Bridge
with penguins.

SB90-15

A SPECIAL DELIVERY
Snowbaby on snowshoes delivers star.

SB90-16

WHO ARE YOU?
Snowbaby and penguin with walrus.

ART CHART #	NAME / TYPE OF PRODUCT	ITEM #	MATERIAL	SET?	🔔	MARKET STATUS	ORIGINAL SRP	GREENBOOK MKT PRICE
					NOTES			
SB90-9	POLAR BEAR LITE-UP, CLIP-ON ORNAMENT (3.5")	7941-3	Porcelain	NO	✓	CURRENT	$ 5.00	$ 5.00
SB90-10	TWINKLE LITTLE STARS FIGURINES (4")	7942-1	Porcelain	SET OF 2		CURRENT	37.50	37.50
	For same subject, miniature, in handpainted pewter, see: 1990 #7621-0 (SB90-1).							
SB90-11	WISHING ON A STAR FIGURINE (3.5")	7943-0	Porcelain	NO		CURRENT	20.00	21.00
	For same subject, miniature, in handpainted pewter, see: 1991 #7626-0 (SB91-13).							
SB90-12	READ ME A STORY! FIGURINE (3.5")	7945-6	Porcelain	NO		CURRENT	25.00	25.00
	For same subject, miniature, in handpainted pewter, see: 1990 #7622-8 (SB90-2).							
SB90-13	WE WILL MAKE IT SHINE! FIGURINE (7.5")	7946-4	Porcelain	NO		CURRENT	45.00	48.00
SB90-14	PLAYING GAMES IS FUN! FIGURINE (5")	7947-2	Porcelain	NO		CURRENT	30.00	32.50
	For same subject, miniature, in handpainted pewter, see: 1990 #7623-6 (SB90-3).							
SB90-15	A SPECIAL DELIVERY FIGURINE (4")	7948-0	Porcelain	NO		CURRENT	13.50	14.00
	For same subject, miniature, in handpainted pewter, see: 1990 #7624-4 (SB90-4).							
SB90-16	WHO ARE YOU? FIGURINE (2.5")	7949-9	Porcelain	NO		LTD. ED. 12,500	32.50	100.00
	Early release to Gift Creations Concepts.							

SNOWBABIES

SB91-1

I'LL PUT UP THE TREE!
Snowbaby holds small tree with star.

SB91-2

WHY DON'T YOU TALK TO ME?
Snowbaby asks snowman a question.

SB91-3

I MADE THIS JUST FOR YOU!
Snowbaby carrying a star wreath.

SB91-4

IS THAT FOR ME?
One Snowbaby holds present
for another.

SB91-5

POLAR SIGN
Penguin looks at Collector's Sign.

SB91-6

THIS IS WHERE WE LIVE!
Snowbaby shows walrus
and polar bear The Pole.

SB91-7

WAITING FOR CHRISTMAS
Two Snowbabies sitting on opposite sides
of present - one watches, one naps.

SB91-8

DANCING TO A TUNE
Snowbaby plays concertina as
two Snowbabies dance.

ART CHART #	NAME / TYPE OF PRODUCT	ITEM #	MATERIAL	SET?	MARKET STATUS / NOTES	ORIGINAL SRP	GREENBOOK MKT PRICE
SB91-1	I'LL PUT UP THE TREE! FIGURINES (4")	6800-4	Porcelain	NO	CURRENT	$ 24.00	$ 24.00
			Early release to Gift Creations Concepts. For same subject, miniature, in handpainted pewter, see: 1991 #7627-9 (SB91-14).					
SB91-2	WHY DON'T YOU TALK TO ME? FIGURINE (4")	6801-2	Porcelain	NO	CURRENT	24.00	24.00
			For same subject, miniature, in handpainted pewter, see: 1991 #7625-2 (SB91-12).					
SB91-3	I MADE THIS JUST FOR YOU! FIGURINE (4.25")	6802-0	Porcelain	NO	CURRENT	15.00	15.00
			For same subject, miniature, in handpainted pewter, see: 1991 #7628-7 (SB91-15).					
SB91-4	IS THAT FOR ME? FIGURINES (4.25")	6803-9	Porcelain	SET OF 2	CURRENT	32.50	32.50
			For same subject, miniature, in handpainted pewter, see: 1991 #7631-7 (SB91-18).					
SB91-5	POLAR SIGN ACCESSORY (3.5")	6804-7	Porcelain	NO	CURRENT	20.00	20.00
SB91-6	THIS IS WHERE WE LIVE! FIGURINE (5")	6805-5	Porcelain	NO	CURRENT	60.00	60.00
SB91-7	WAITING FOR CHRISTMAS FIGURINE (2.75")	6807-1	Porcelain	NO	CURRENT	27.50	27.50
			For same subject, miniature, in handpainted pewter, see: 1991 #7629-5 (SB91-16).					
SB91-8	DANCING TO A TUNE FIGURINES (4")	6808-0	Porcelain	SET OF 3	CURRENT	30.00	30.00
			For same subject, miniature, in handpainted pewter, see: 1991 #7630-9 (SB91-17).					

208

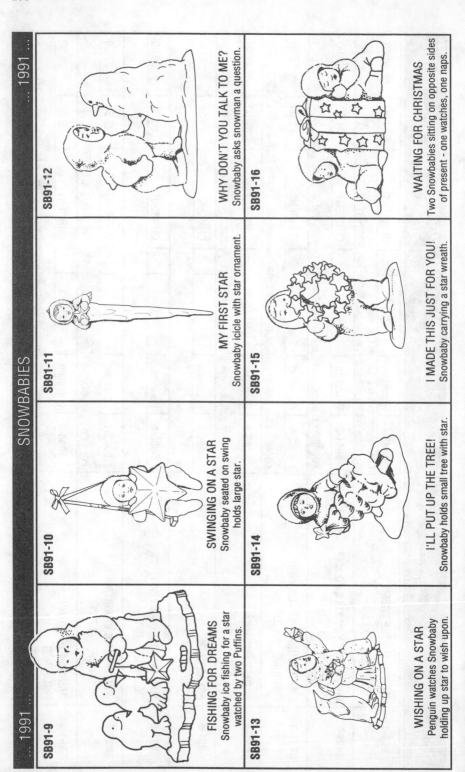

SB91-9

FISHING FOR DREAMS
Snowbaby ice fishing for a star watched by two Puffins.

SB91-10

SWINGING ON A STAR
Snowbaby seated on swing holds large star.

SB91-11

MY FIRST STAR
Snowbaby icicle with star ornament.

SB91-12

WHY DON'T YOU TALK TO ME?
Snowbaby asks snowman a question.

SB91-13

WISHING ON A STAR
Penguin watches Snowbaby holding up star to wish upon.

SB91-14

I'LL PUT UP THE TREE!
Snowbaby holds small tree with star.

SB91-15

I MADE THIS JUST FOR YOU!
Snowbaby carrying a star wreath.

SB91-16

WAITING FOR CHRISTMAS
Two Snowbabies sitting on opposite sides of present - one watches, one naps.

ART CHART #	NAME / TYPE OF PRODUCT	ITEM #	MATERIAL	SET?	☻ MARKET STATUS	ORIGINAL SRP	GREENBOOK MKT PRICE
					NOTES		
SB91-9	FISHING FOR DREAMS FIGURINE (4")	6809-8	Porcelain	NO	CURRENT	$ 28.00	$ 28.00
SB91-10	SWINGING ON A STAR ORNAMENT (3.5")	6810-1	Porcelain	NO	CURRENT	9.50	9.50
SB91-11	MY FIRST STAR ORNAMENT (6.75")	6811-0	Porcelain	NO	CURRENT	7.00	7.00
SB91-12	WHY DON'T YOU TALK TO ME? MINIATURES (1.5")	7625-2	Pewter	SET OF 2	CURRENT	12.00	12.00
	For same subject, full size, in porcelain, see: 1991 #6801-2 (SB91-2).						
SB91-13	WISHING ON A STAR MINIATURE (1.25")	7626-0	Pewter	NO	CURRENT	10.00	10.00
	For same subject, full size, in porcelain, see: 1990 #7943-0 (SB90-11).						
SB91-14	I'LL PUT UP THE TREE! MINIATURE (1.25")	7627-9	Pewter	NO	CURRENT	9.00	9.00
	For same subject, full size, in porcelain, see: 1991 #6800-4 (SB91-1).						
SB91-15	I MADE THIS JUST FOR YOU! MINIATURE (1.25")	7628-7	Pewter	NO	CURRENT	7.00	7.00
	For same subject, full size, in porcelain, see: 1991 #6802-0 (SB91-3).						
SB91-16	WAITING FOR CHRISTMAS MINIATURE (1.25")	7629-5	Pewter	NO	CURRENT	12.50	12.50
	For same subject, full size, in porcelain, see: 1991 #6807-1 (SB91-7).						

SNOWBABIES

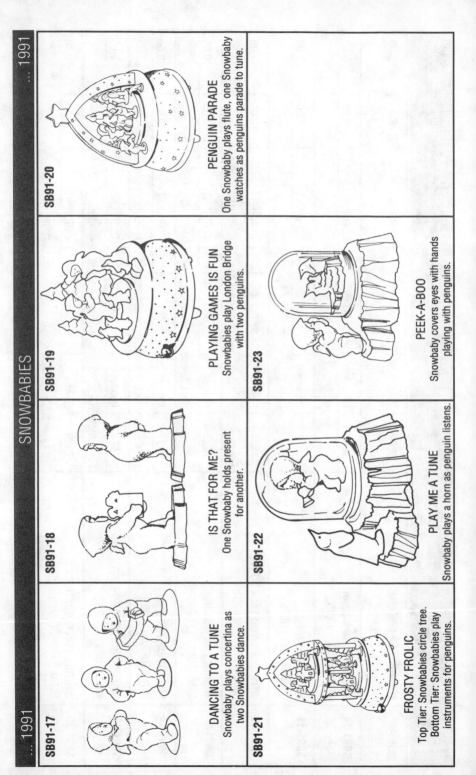

SB91-17

DANCING TO A TUNE
Snowbaby plays concertina as
two Snowbabies dance.

SB91-18

IS THAT FOR ME?
One Snowbaby holds present
for another.

SB91-19

PLAYING GAMES IS FUN
Snowbabies play London Bridge
with two penguins.

SB91-20

PENGUIN PARADE
One Snowbaby plays flute, one Snowbaby
watches as penguins parade to tune.

SB91-21

FROSTY FROLIC
Top Tier: Snowbabies circle tree.
Bottom Tier: Snowbabies play
instruments for penguins.

SB91-22

PLAY ME A TUNE
Snowbaby plays a horn as penguin listens.

SB91-23

PEEK-A-BOO
Snowbaby covers eyes with hands
playing with penguins.

ART CHART #	NAME TYPE OF PRODUCT	ITEM #	MATERIAL	SET?	❂ MARKET STATUS	ORIGINAL SRP	GREENBOOK MKT PRICE
SB91-17	**DANCING TO A TUNE** MINIATURES (1.5")	7630-9	Pewter	SET OF 3	CURRENT	$ 18.00	$ 18.00
			NOTES: For same subject, full size, in porcelain, see: 1991 #6808-0 (SB91-8).				
SB91-18	**IS THAT FOR ME?** MINIATURES (1.5")	7631-7	Pewter	SET OF 2	CURRENT	12.50	12.50
			NOTES: For same subject, full size, in porcelain, see: 1991 #6803-9 (SB91-4).				
SB91-19	**PLAYING GAMES IS FUN!** REVOLVING MUSIC BOX (6")	7632-5	Wood/Resin	NO	CURRENT	72.00	72.00
			NOTES: Tune: "Twinkle, Twinkle Little Star."				
SB91-20	**PENGUIN PARADE** REVOLVING MUSIC BOX (7")	7633-3	Wood/Resin	NO	CURRENT	72.00	72.00
			NOTES: Tune: "Brahms Lullaby."				
SB91-21	**FROSTY FROLIC** 2-TIER MUSIC BOX (10.25")	7634-1	Wood/Resin	NO	CURRENT	110.00	110.00
			NOTES: Tune: "Let It Snow."				
SB91-22	**PLAY ME A TUNE** WATERGLOBE/MUSIC BOX (5")	7936-7	Bisque	NO	CURRENT	50.00	50.00
			NOTES: Tune: "Joy To The World."				
SB91-23	**PEEK-A-BOO** WATERGLOBE/MUSIC BOX (6.5")	7938-3	Bisque	NO	CURRENT	50.00	50.00
			NOTES: Tune: "Let It Snow."				

SNOWBABIES

SB92-1

CAN I HELP, TOO?
Snowbaby seated on polar bear places star on tree. Second Snowbaby holds up another star. Penguin greets bear.

SB92-2

WAIT FOR ME!
Snowbaby pushes sleigh filled with presents and stars as two penguins follow.

SB92-3

I NEED A HUG
Two Snowbabies hug.

SB92-4

WINKEN, BLINKEN, AND NOD
Three Snowbabies in star trimmed boat with waves lapping at base.
One Snowbaby and penguin scan the horizon. One Snowbaby naps at rear of boat. Middle Snowbaby holds stars.

SB92-5

LET'S GO SKIING!
Snowbaby holds skis.

SB92-6

not pictured

THIS WILL CHEER YOU UP

ART CHART #	NAME TYPE OF PRODUCT	ITEM #	MATERIAL	SET?	MARKET STATUS	ORIGINAL SRP	GREENBOOK MKT PRICE
					NOTES		
SB92-1	CAN I HELP, TOO? FIGURINE (5")	6806-3	Porcelain	NO	LTD. ED. 18,500	$ 48.00	$ 48.00
SB92-2	WAIT FOR ME! FIGURINE (4.5")	6812-8	Porcelain	NO	CURRENT	48.00	48.00
SB92-3	I NEED A HUG FIGURINE (4.25")	6813-6	Porcelain	NO	CURRENT	20.00	20.00
SB92-4	WINKEN, BLINKEN, AND NOD FIGURINE (5")	6814-4	Porcelain	NO	CURRENT	60.00	60.00
	Early release to Gift Creations Concepts.						
SB92-5	LET'S GO SKIING! FIGURINE (4.5")	6815-2	Porcelain	NO	CURRENT	15.00	15.00
SB92-6	THIS WILL CHEER YOU UP FIGURINE (4.25")	6816-0	Porcelain	NO	CURRENT	30.00	30.00
	Early release to Ideation.						

RETIRED ORIGINAL SNOW VILLAGE

5000-8	1984	TOWN HALL	5048-2	1988	CHURCH OF THE OPEN DOOR
5001-3	1979	MOUNTAIN LODGE	5049-0	1987	SPRUCE PLACE
5001-6	1985	GROCERY	5050-4	1987	DUPLEX
5002-1	1979	GABLED COTTAGE	5051-2	1988	DEPOT AND TRAIN
5002-4	1984	VICTORIAN COTTAGE			WITH 2 TRAIN CARS
5003-2	1985	GOVERNOR'S MANSION	5052-0	1987	RIDGEWOOD
5003-9	1979	THE INN	5054-2	1982	VICTORIAN
5004-0	1986	TURN OF THE CENTURY	5054-7	1990	KENWOOD HOUSE
5004-7	1979	COUNTRY CHURCH	5055-9	1981	KNOB HILL
5005-4	1979	STEEPLED CHURCH	5056-7	1981	BROWNSTONE
5005-9	1986	MAIN STREET HOUSE	5057-5	1981	LOG CABIN
5006-2	1979	SMALL CHALET	5058-3	1984	COUNTRYSIDE CHURCH
5006-7	1989	ST. ANTHONY HOTEL &	5059-1	1980	STONE CHURCH
		POST OFFICE	5060-1	1988	LINCOLN PARK DUPLEX
5007-0	1979	VICTORIAN HOUSE	5060-9	1982	SCHOOL HOUSE
5007-5	1986	STRATFORD HOUSE	5061-7	1981	TUDOR HOUSE
5008-3	1987	HAVERSHAM HOUSE	5062-5	1980	MISSION CHURCH
5008-8	1979	MANSION	5062-8	1988	SONOMA HOUSE
5009-1	1985	GALENA HOUSE	5063-3	1980	MOBILE HOME
5009-6	1979	STONE CHURCH	5063-6	1988	HIGHLAND PARK HOUSE
5010-5	1987	RIVER ROAD HOUSE	5065-2	1988	BEACON HILL HOUSE
5011-2	1984	HOMESTEAD	5065-8	1982	GIANT TREES
5012-0	1980	GENERAL STORE	5066-0	1988	PACIFIC HEIGHTS HOUSE
5012-1	1986	DELTA HOUSE	5066-6	1980	ADOBE HOUSE
5013-0	1989	SNOW VILLAGE FACTORY	5067-4	1981	CATHEDRAL CHURCH
5013-8	1980	CAPE COD	5067-9	1989	RAMSEY HILL HOUSE
5014-6	1986	NANTUCKET	5068-2	1982	STONE MILL HOUSE
5015-3	1979	SKATING RINK /	5068-7	1988	SAINT JAMES CHURCH
		DUCK POND SET	5070-9	1982	COLONIAL FARM HOUSE
5015-6	1986	BAYPORT	5071-7	1988	CARRIAGE HOUSE
5016-1	1989	SMALL DOUBLE TREES	5071-7	1982	TOWN CHURCH
5017-2	1984	SKATING POND	5072-5	1984	WOODEN CLAPBOARD
5019-9	1990	CATHEDRAL CHURCH	5073-3	1982	ENGLISH COTTAGE
5019-9	1984	STREET CAR	5073-3	1990	TOY SHOP
5020-2	1984	CENTENNIAL HOUSE	5074-1	1984	BARN
5021-0	1984	CARRIAGE HOUSE	5076-8	1990	APOTHECARY
5022-9	1984	PIONEER CHURCH	5076-8	1983	CORNER STORE
5023-7	1984	SWISS CHALET	5077-6	1983	BAKERY
5024-5	1983	BANK	5077-6	1991	BAKERY
5025-3	1984	GINGERBREAD HOUSE	5078-4	1987	DINER
5026-1	1984	VILLAGE CHURCH	5078-4	1982	ENGLISH CHURCH
5027-0	1990	SPRINGFIELD HOUSE	5080-6	1989	LARGE SINGLE TREE
5028-8	1986	GOTHIC CHURCH	5081-4	1983	GABLED HOUSE
5029-6	1985	PARSONAGE	5082-2	1983	FLOWER SHOP
5030-0	1988	LIGHTHOUSE	5082-2	1991	JEFFERSON SCHOOL
5031-8	1985	WOODEN CHURCH	5083-0	1984	NEW STONE CHURCH
5032-6	1984	FIRE STATION	5084-9	1984	CHATEAU
5033-4	1985	ENGLISH TUDOR	5085-6	1985	TRAIN STATION WITH
5034-2	1985	CONGREGATIONAL CHURCH			3 TRAIN CARS
5035-0	1986	TRINITY CHURCH	5091-1	1989	FIRE STATION NO. 2
5036-9	1985	SUMMIT HOUSE	5092-0	1989	SNOW VILLAGE RESORT LODGE
5037-7	1986	NEW SCHOOL HOUSE	5114-4	1991	JINGLE BELLE HOUSEBOAT
5039-3	1986	PARISH CHURCH	5121-7	1990	MAPLE RIDGE INN
5041-5	1986	WAVERLY PLACE	5124-1	1991	CORNER CAFE
5042-3	1986	TWIN PEAKS	5125-0	1990	SINGLE CAR GARAGE
5043-1	1986	2101 MAPLE	5126-8	1991	HOME SWEET HOME/
5044-0	1991	VILLAGE MARKET			HOUSE & WINDMILL
5045-8	1986	STUCCO BUNGALOW	5128-4	1991	SERVICE STATION
5046-6	1988	WILLIAMSBURG HOUSE	5141-1	1990	PALOS VERDES
5047-4	1987	PLANTATION HOUSE			

RETIRED MEADOWLAND

5050-0	1980	THATCHED COTTEAGE	5052-6	1980	ASPEN TREES
5051-8	1980	COUNTRYSIDE CHURCH	5053-4	1980	SHEEP

RETIRED ORIGINAL SNOW VILLAGE ACCESSORIES

5018-0	1990	SNOWMAN WITH BROOM	5108-0	1989	FOR SALE SIGN
5038-5	1985	SCOTTIE WITH TREE	5113-6	1990	SNOW KIDS
5040-7	1988	MONKS-A-CAROLING	5117-9	1990	HAYRIDE
5053-9	1987	SINGING NUNS	5118-7	1990	SCHOOL CHILDREN
5056-3	1987	SNOW KIDS SLED, SKIS	5129-2	1990	APPLE GIRL/NEWSPAPER BOY
5057-1	1988	FAMILY MOM/KIDS, GOOSE/GIRL	5130-6	1991	WOODSMAN AND BOY
5059-8	1988	SANTA/MAILBOX	5133-0	1991	WATER TOWER
5064-1	1986	CAROLERS	5136-5	1990	WOODY STATION WAGON
5069-0	1986	CERAMIC CAR	5137-3	1991	SCHOOL BUS, SNOW PLOW
5079-2	1986	CERAMIC SLEIGH	5148-9	1990	SPECIAL DELIVERY
5094-6	1990	KIDS AROUND THE TREE	5168-3	1991	KIDS TREE HOUSE
5095-4	1987	GIRL/SNOWMAN, BOY	5170-5	1991	SKATE FASTER MOM
5096-2	1988	SHOPPING GIRLS WITH PACKAGES	5172-1	1991	THROUGH THE WOODS
5102-0	1988	3 NUNS W/SONGBOOKS	5173-0	1991	STATUE OF MARK TWAIN
5103-9	1988	PRAYING MONKS	5174-8	1991	CALLING ALL CARS
5104-7	1989	CHILDREN IN BAND	5179-9	1990	MAILBOX
5105-5	1990	CAROLING FAMILY	6459-9	1984	MONKS-A-CAROLING
5107-1	1990	CHRISTMAS CHILDREN	8183-3	1991	SISAL TREE LOT

RETIRED DICKENS' VILLAGE

5583-2	1991	COBLES POLICE STATION	6508-0	1990	BLYTHE POND MILL HOUSE
5900-5	1989	BARLEY BREE	6515-3	1988	THE ORIGINAL SHOPS OF
5900-5	1989	FARMHOUSE			DICKENS' VILLAGE
5900-5	1989	BARN	6515-3	1988	CROWNTREE INN
5902-1	1990	COUNTING HOUSE &	6515-3	1988	CANDLE SHOP
		SILAS THIMBLETON BARRISTER	6515-3	1988	GREEN GROCER
5916-1	1988	KENILWORTH CASTLE	6515-3	1988	GOLDEN SWAN BAKER
5924-2	1990	COBBLESTONE SHOPS	6515-3	1988	BEAN AND SON SMITHY SHOP
5924-2	1990	THE WOOL SHOP	6515-3	1988	ABEL BEESLEY BUTCHER
5924-2	1990	BOOTER AND COBBLER	6515-3	1988	JONES & CO. BRUSH &
5924-2	1990	T. WELLS FRUIT & SPICE SHOP			BASKET SHOP
5925-0	1991	NICHOLAS NICKLEBY	6516-1	1989	DICKENS' VILLAGE CHURCH
5925-0	1991	NICHOLAS NICKLEBY COTTAGE	6518-8	1988	DICKENS' COTTAGES
5925-0	1991	WACKFORD SQUEERS BOARDING SCHOOL	6518-8	1988	THATCHED COTTAGE
5927-7	1991	IVY GLEN CHURCH	6518-8	1988	STONE COTTAGE
6507-2	1989	DICKENS' LANE SHOPS	6518-8	1988	TUDOR COTTAGE
6507-2	1989	THOMAS KERSEY COFFEE HOUSE	6528-5	1989	CHADBURY STATION
6507-2	1989	COTTAGE TOY SHOP			AND TRAIN
6507-2	1989	TUTTLES PUB	6549-8	1989	BRICK ABBEY

RETIRED NEW ENGLAND VILLAGE

5931-5	1989	WESTON TRAIN STATION	6530-7	1989	LIVERY STABLE & BOOT SHOP
5939-0	1990	CHERRY LANE SHOPS	6530-7	1989	STEEPLE CHURCH
5939-0	1990	BEN'S BARBERSHOP	6530-7	1989	BRICK TOWN HALL
5939-0	1990	OTIS HAYES BUTCHER SHOP	6530-7	1989	RED SCHOOLHOUSE
5939-0	1990	ANNE SHAW TOYS	6530-7	1989	NATHANIEL BINGHAM FABRICS
5940-4	1991	ADA'S BED AND BOARDING HOUSE	6538-2	1989	JACOB ADAMS FARMHOUSE
5942-0	1991	BERKSHIRE HOUSE			& BARN
6530-7	1989	NEW ENGLAND VILLAGE	6539-0	1990	STEEPLE CHURCH
6530-7	1989	APOTHECARY SHOP	6544-7	1990	TIMBER KNOLL LOG CABIN
6530-7	1989	GENERAL STORE			

RETIRED ALPINE VILLAGE

5952-8	1989	JOSEF ENGEL FARMHOUSE
6541-2	1991	ALPINE CHURCH

RETIRED CHRISTMAS IN THE CITY

5961-7	1989	SUTTON PLACE BROWNSTONES
5962-5	1990	THE CATHEDRAL
5963-3	1989	PALACE THEATRE
5968-4	1991	CHOCOLATE SHOPPE
5969-2	1991	CITY HALL
5972-2	1990	VARIETY STORE
6512-9	1990	CHRISTMAS IN THE CITY
6512-9	1990	TOY SHOP & PET STORE
6512-9	1990	BAKERY
6512-9	1990	TOWER RESTAURANT

RETIRED HERITAGE VILLAGE ACCESSORIES

5579-4	1991	CONSTABLES	5983-8	1991	CITY BUS & MILK TRUCK
5901-3	1989	FARM PEOPLE & ANIMALS	5985-4	1991	SALVATION ARMY BAND
5903-0	1991	CHILDE POND AND SKATERS	5986-2	1990	WOODCUTTER AND SON
5928-5	1990	FEZZIWIG AND FRIENDS	6501-3	1990	CHRISTMAS CAROL FIGURES
5929-3	1991	NICHOLAS NICKLEBY CHARACTERS	6510-2	1989	LIGHTED TREE W/CHILDREN
5934-0	1990	BLACKSMITH			& LADDER
5941-2	1991	VILLAGE HARVEST PEOPLE	6511-0	1990	SLEIGHRIDE
5945-5	1991	FARM ANIMALS	6526-9	1990	CAROLERS
5950-1	1989	SILO & HAY SHED	6527-7	1986	VILLAGE TRAIN
5951-0	1989	OX SLED	6531-5	1990	COVERED WOODED BRIDGE
5957-9	1991	ORGAN GRINDER	6532-3	1990	NEW ENGLAND WINTER SET
5959-5	1991	RIVER STREET ICE HOUSE CART	6545-5	1990	SKATING POND
5965-0	1990	CITY PEOPLE	6546-3	1990	STONE BRIDGE
5966-8	1988	SHOPKEEPERS	6547-1	1989	VILLAGE WELL & HOLY CROSS
5967-6	1988	CITY WORKERS	6589-7	1989	MAPLE SUGARING SHED
5971-4	1991	CITY NEWSSTAND	6590-0	1990	DOVER COACH
5981-1	1990	VILLAGE TRAIN TRESTLE			

RETIRED SNOWBABIES

7730-5	1989	ALLISON & DUNCAN
7950-2	1987	CATCH A FALLING STAR
7952-9	1990	SNOWBABY SITTING
7954-5	1990	SNOWBABY WINGED
7955-3	1990	GIVE ME A PUSH!
7958-8	1989	BEST FRIENDS
7959-6	1989	SNOWBABY NITE LITE
7961-8	1989	SNOWBABY ON BRASS RIBBON ORNAMENT
7964-2	1987	SNOWBABY STANDING
7965-0	1989	SNOWBABY CLIMBING ON SNOWBALL
7966-9	1989	SNOWBABIES HANGING PAIR
7967-7	1987	CATCH A FALLING STAR
7968-5	1990	DON'T FALL OFF!
7969-3	1990	SNOWBABY ADRIFT
7970-7	1987	SNOWBABY HOLDING PICTURE FRAME
7971-5	1989	SNOWBABY CLIMBING ON TREE
7973-1	1988	SNOWBABY WITH WINGS
7975-8	1988	SNOWBABIES RIDING SLEDS
7979-0	1990	TINY TRIO
7980-4	1990	TWINKLE LITTLE STAR
7983-9	1991	FROSTY FUN
7984-7	1991	ALL FALL DOWN

DICKENS' VILLAGE LIMITED EDITIONS

5585-9	RUTH MARION SCOTCH WOOLEN	17,500
5586-7	GREEN GATE COTTAGE	22,500
5904-8	C. FLETCHER PUBLIC HOUSE	12,500
6502-1	NORMAN CHURCH	3,500
6519-6	DICKENS' VILLAGE MILL	2,500
6568-4	CHESTERTON MANOR HOUSE	7,500

NEW ENGLAND VILLAGE LIMITED EDITIONS

| 6543-1 | SMYTHE WOOLEN MILL | 7,500 |

CHRISTMAS IN THE CITY LIMITED EDITIONS

| 5549-2 | CATHEDRAL CHURCH OF ST. MARK | 17,500 |
| 5974-9 | DOROTHY'S DRESS SHOP | 12,500 |

SNOWBABIES LIMITED EDITIONS

6806-3	CAN I HELP, TOO?	18,500
7949-9	WHO ARE YOU?	12,500
7981-2	FROSTY FROLIC	4,800
7985-2	FINDING FALLEN STARS	6,000

220

NAME...DEPT. 56 ITEM #...GREENBOOK ART CHART #...PAGE #...VILLAGE INDEX

THE GREENBOOK GUIDE TO THE
ENESCO PRECIOUS MOMENTS COLLECTION,
SEVENTH EDITION
ISBN 0-923628-12-6

THE GREENBOOK GUIDE TO ORNAMENTS
INCLUDING THE HALLMARK KEEPSAKE,
ENESCO TREASURY OF CHRISTMAS,
& CARLTON/SUMMIT HEIRLOOM COLLECTIONS,
THIRD EDITION
ISBN 0-923628-14-2

THE GREENBOOK GUIDE TO THE
MEMORIES OF YESTERDAY COLLECTION
BY ENESCO,
THIRD EDITION
ISBN 0-923628-11-8

...WE JUST WANTED YOU TO SEE...

Department 56 collectibles are hand crafted. Differences occur naturally as a result of firing and painting, can be an announced production change, or the result of human error. On the following pages are some of the variations that have generated a great deal of interest among collectors and on the secondary market. Perhaps until now you've heard about them or seen them advertised but never had the opportunity to do a side by side comparison...

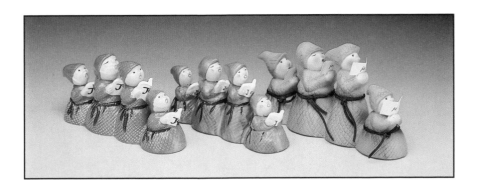

MONKS-A-CAROLING
6459-9 SVA83-5
5040-7 SVA84-7

Variation: Actually are three variations. The two glazed versions are differentiated by the coloration on the cheeks. In 1983, *(left)* the cheeks had a diffused rosy blush. In 1984, *(middle)* a circular rose shape/color gave the cheeks a blush. The matte finish *(right)* is larger than the other two and has the Monks holding paper songbooks, wearing rope belts, and each with a distinct facial expression. The 1983 glazed and 1984 matte pieces were originally part of the Department 56 Christmas giftware line. Based on the popularity of incorporating them in the Original Snow Village, the 1984 set was produced.

CAROLERS
6526-9 HVA84-1

Variation: Two versions encompass a design change (re-sculpted) as well as a color change. The first version *(right)* is known as the "original white post."

DOVER COACH
6590-0 HVA87-26

Variation: Original production *(right)* showed a clean shaven coachman (the gent who rides at the rear and sounds the coaching horn). Second version produced a mustache on the same person.

DICKENS' VILLAGE CHURCH
6516-1 DV85-1

Variation: Color descriptions ranging from the elusive "winter white" to
(left to right) "green," "cream," "tan," and a version simply termed
"dark." This is possibly the most discussed, confusing, and subjective
color variation in the Collection.

PEGGOTTY'S SEASIDE COTTAGE
5550-6 DV89-4

Variation: Distinct color change was addressed by Department 56 in their Winter 1990 Newsletter: "When the Peggotty's Seaside Cottage piece was introduced in May, the handpainted hulls were produced with a tan color because the textured surface would not 'accept' the dark green color indicated in the artist's renderings. The Master Painters have since developed a new technique which allows the piece to be painted a uniform shade of deep green as originally intended, and 1991 production pieces will display the green hull."

STEEPLE CHURCH
6530-7 NE86-6
6539-0 NE89-4

Variation: Design change in mold. First design issued, 6530-7 *(right)*, has the front tree as actual part of the mold. When viewed straight on, the tree does not touch the ground and appears level with front step. The re-issue, 6539-0 *(left)*, has a separate, glued on tree. When viewed straight on, the tree rests on the "ground." Color variations have also been noted between the two designs.

THE FLAT OF EBENEZER SCROOGE
5587-5 DV89-11

Variation: Windows without any panes *(left)*.

ADA'S BED AND BOARDING HOUSE
5940-4 NE88-6

Variation: Three variations have been noted encompassing both mold and color changes. First is original mold and "lemon gold" color *(left)*, second is original mold and "cream" color *(middle)*, third is the new mold *(right)*. The new mold is easily identified by the attached rear steps with no surrounding snow, the different windows, and size of dormers.

BERKSHIRE HOUSE
5942-0 NE89-1

Variation: Color change produced two versions: "original blue" *(right)* and "teal" *(left)*.

AMISH FAMILY
5948-0 HVA90-66

Variation: Set was introduced with the father bearded and with a mustache. Amish men do not have mustaches, current production has a clean upper lip.

CITY HALL
5969-2 CIC88-2

Variation: Smaller in size "Proof" version *(left)*, next to the normal piece *(right)*.

REINDEER BARN
5601-4 NP90-3

Variation: Naming Santa's reindeer should be easy. However confusion during production produced a variation with Comet's name appearing twice.